C000001100

Designed in collaboration with Soka Studio Ltd

Cover artwork by Peter K Rollings

This edition printed 2022 by Ruddocks
56 Great Northern Terrace, Lincoln LN5 8HL

ISBN 978-0-904327-35-9

The proceeds from this book will go towards a new kitchen.

Content advisory warning:
Contains infinity loops which may absorb the unwary reader.
Generally inoffensive, despite occasional fictional violence,
animal cruelty, imprisonment and death. One explicit nude
imprint of a bum and one apparent scrotum.

INVENTORY

Brick dust
Letter

INVENTORY

Brick dust
Letter

INVENTORY

Brick dust
Letter

Page intentionally blank

Welcome to Smorgasboard, Adventurer!

I mean, I say "welcome", it's the standard greeting and
they pay me to say it, so I must. Apparently, if I say it
with a smile it comes across better. "A warm greeting with
a smile!" that's what they told us during training. But they
don't have to hang around on page five forever, waiting for
the next mug to flick past the first few pages, do they?
Never a day off, not even bank holidays. Did you read any of
page two or did you just skim over the ISBN number? No, no
one ever bothers.

Anyway, Welcome to Smorgasboard, Adventurer! Adventurer?
Well, that remains to be seen. 'Punter' would be more
appropriate if you ask me. But no one does. To be honest,
I've got better things to do, but since you're here we may
as well get on with it. Don't get me wrong, but the ones
who came before you, well, I just don't hold out much hope.

Firstly, cut out a bookmark from page three and use it to
save your progress. You can physically move yourself across
the page for extra fun as you follow the path! Could you
tell I was smiling then?

Right, this is you.

Nice hat. You've entered the Smorgasboard, obviously.
This world is a game that you must play your way across.
A puzzle, if you will. Will you? Mostly you'll read the text
to work out the route ahead, but sometimes the board will
present itself as an actual map on the page.

The rules are self-explanatory, and I'm pretty tired. I'm sure you'll work it out - just make sure you read carefully. You shouldn't need it, but if you get really lost, try constructing a map. You can use the final page to draw on.

Off you go then, follow the path. It heads across the bridge over there and will take you to the board proper. This is just page six, the staging area where we prepare all the punters before they get sent off to their doom. On their quest, I mean! Just a nice quest. That's what they said to tell you, at the training course.

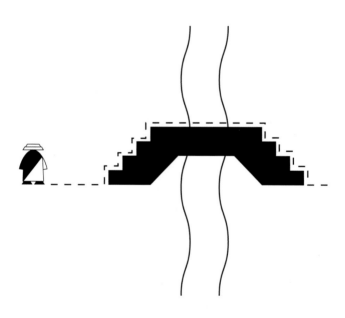

Just as you cross the river, you hear dark laughter on the cold, northerly wind, quickly followed by a thunderous crumbling – the bridge has collapsed behind you! In addition to this, you are covered in brick dust.

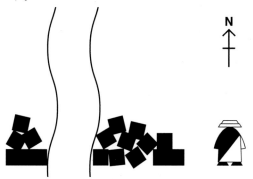

Oh, by the way, you can't leave. Yes, sorry about that. Look, there's no way back. The river is a torrent; too wide to jump across, too treacherous to swim, you never learnt to canoe, and there isn't one anyway.

Looks like you're trapped!

You can't leave the Smorgasboard. By order of Baron Smorg. He's in charge around here; owns the whole place, never does any work, your standard aristocrat.

Every cloud has a silver lining, though! In this case, the breeze peels back the silvery clouds above you to reveal a floating north pointer in the sky. That should come in useful to find your way around! Let's just hope you don't have to go underground...

Oh, by the way, what's your name? I can't be calling you Adventurer the whole time. Do you mind Punter? A bit offensive, I suppose. Let's see, you'll be doing a lot of walking across the board - what about Pedestrian? No, Pawn? Prisoner? What about just P? Let's go with P.

Nice to meet you, P. I'm the narrator. I'll try to stop you from going astray, if I remember to, but I can't actually intervene. I'm just a narrator after all, not a guide. Saying that, if I sound worried that you're going the wrong way I suggest you pay attention, although no one ever does.

As you stand there looking forlorn, a tingling sensation suddenly overcomes you, as if someone is blowing glitter in your face and stroking your hair. Your sight clouds over, and you have a vision of a sad-looking clown trapped in a dank cell.

Although all clowns look sad, this one isn't pretending. His juggling paraphernalia litter the cell, abandoned. Weeping, the clown slowly spins a plate on one finger and pushes a meagre portion of gruel into his mouth with the other hand. He looks up, and the plate clatters to the floor as he seems to notice your presence!

As the vision fades, the clown leaps to his feet and shouts towards you in desperation, but you can't hear him. As suddenly as you arrived, you return to the riverbank with the collapsed bridge behind you.

What was that, P? You zoned out for a moment there. That's strange. Nothing like that ever happened with any of the others.

You look down to see a sealed envelope has appeared in your hand. The seal bears the symbol of Smorg. You open it to read the letter inside.

Dear Sir or Madam,

HELP!

Adventurer, Oh, thanks above. You are here, and not a moment to lose!

My name is Bongo, I am the official bard to Baron Smorg. I have been imprisoned in the Baron's castle, and like you, I must escape this place! I would be forever grateful to you if you could rescue me.

Let me reiterate - please HELP!! In exchange, I believe that I can help you escape back to your own world from this papery realm. In my years entertaining the Baron at court, I have overheard him occasionally talk of the secret to this - it is held in the castle itself!

If this letter has reached you, then the first part of my plan has been a success, but I fear that I will not be able to risk writing to you directly beyond this. I've managed to convince the guard that I have written this letter to my elderly mother when in reality, I've had it delivered to a friendly sprite who owes me a favour - I hope you like glitter! Don't ask.

I hope the risk has been worth it and this message finds you safely. If the Baron finds out that I have been allowed to correspond with the outside world without his approval, well, who can say how I will be punished. . .

However, I have left clues to help you navigate across the Smorgasboard - cunningly, I have concealed these in plain sight! In my role as court jester, I am in charge of publishing all the poems, puns, riddles, jokes and plays to entertain the citizens of the board. The Baron likes to distract the populace from his crimes with humour.

The signposts on your journey will display my literary works - decipher the hints contained within to assist you in finding your way to the castle! I'm afraid I've had to be a little cryptic to avoid arousing the Baron's suspicions. Be warned, Adventurer, Smorgasboard can be a bit of a maze!

The Baron built this place as a labyrinth to be impenetrable to enemies. Only he knows all of Smorgasboard's secrets, and you yet have far to journey, but in general, I believe his castle to be roughly northeast of Board #1.

One final tip – don't listen to the narrator – he's just a disembodied voice! He's very unreliable. The Baron has been thinking about getting rid of him, if you know what I mean. At best, he won't be concentrating. At worst, he could be actively misleading you – he certainly can't be trusted.

I hope against hope for your quest to succeed!

Yours, Bongo

Oh, you've got a letter – from Bongo, was it? That bloody Jester. Tedious.

Take a closer look at your bookmark; I've **added the letter** to your inventory, but in future you'll have to do this yourself. If you lose an item, ~~cross it out~~. Collecting items or gaining knowledge on your travels will enable your decision-making. You do not need to duplicate an item if you already have one. If your memory is as dreadful as I suspect, consider jotting down the location of, or requirement for, certain items. You can use the map page. Do feel free to try without, though. Prove me wrong!

Anyway, Bongo creates all the supposedly hilarious content to be found in Smorgasboard, under pain of death. You'll find it shown on signposts around the place. Confusingly, these are also called boards; Smorgas-boards. You can think of them as signposts. Personally, I don't think he's very amusing. Not easy to be funny under his circumstances, I suppose.

Oh, there's the first signpost up ahead. I guess you'd better have a look, if you can put up with it. It's over there, on the opposite page. In general, you should turn the page to continue the story unless instructed otherwise. That's how books work!

Board #1
Bing bong!

I would do anything for flumps,
but I won't do that!

Love and smiles!
Yours, Bongo

Mm. You walk beyond the signpost. Move your bookmark effigy across the page — that's right.

You arrive at a junction with two paths to choose from, heading north or south.

If you perish, you will be transported back here to start again. I'll keep a tally...

If you are restarting after an unfortunate demise, cross out all items from your inventory other than brick dust and letter. No cheating!

Well, it's up to you now, P.

Do you want to head North or South? Not that I care.

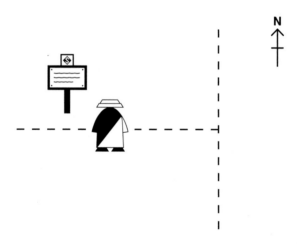

Proceed North – turn to page 13.

OR

Proceed South – turn to page 16.

The proceedings commence! A way up the trail, the path becomes bounded by two high walls and starts to resemble a wide driveway. An ornate gateway is closed to you up ahead. The symbol of Smorg is wrought into the metalwork. This must be castle road, a shortcut to the Baron's citadel! Beyond the gate, a black causeway leads across the board into the distance. It feels like private land, with no public right of way.

The Baron controls most of the land around here, I'm afraid. You can't just wander off anywhere. He's very powerful and has total jurisdiction over spelling, although apparently he struggles with punctuation. That's what I've heard from others anyway, but it could just be rumour. I've only met him once, our monarch, when I graduated from the training course. He gave a terrific speech with lots of big ideas for the future. Sorry if I seem intentionally ambiguous; I can't help it. Sometimes, my language can have multiple meanings. Here I am talking too much about myself, sorry – let's focus on you, for all the good it will do.

Where were we? Oh yes, you can't just wander off anywhere – that would be anarchy, and I won't have any hand in it. Your options are fixed, see below.

You creep closer to the gate but freeze as you notice a band of the Baron's soldiers lounging outside the gatehouse. The symbol of Smorg is emblazoned on their breasts. They haven't spotted you yet. They are busy looting the body of a previous adventurer who was bold enough to come this way. You pat yourself down, checking your pockets for useful items, but your inventory is meagre, and you have no inherited wealth to gain advantage here. It's not too late to turn back, P. Take the hint.

Time to retreat?

To turn back and head south, turn to page 12.

OR

To advance upon the soldiers, continue to page 14.

What are you doing, P?

Outnumbered, with no weapons, no skill, and covered in brick dust, you charge at the Baron's soldiers!

You bounce off the first one, hitting the floor hard. The noise of looting ceases, and all the soldiers crane their necks to look at their attacker.

Your head spinning, you sit up just in time to see a large, webbed foot slam itself into your face. Your vision swims, and you fall back on the pavement.

A good thumping ensues, and you taste blood in your mouth. You sense this may be your end. How disappointing. Such a waste of a nice hat. Oh well, I'll probably just head back to page five and wait for the next victim.

You feel an overwhelming sense of failure wash over you. Failure and – what's that? Mixed in with the blood, you can taste – feathers?

You black out and are no more.

Turn to page 12.

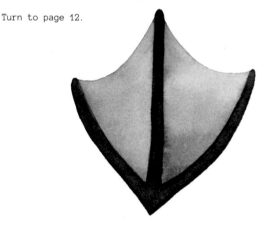

After some time on the road, you come across an old
encampment. The remnants of a fire and the litter give
it away – people were here! Unfortunately, smorgrass has
started to grow over the campsite debris; it seems it was
last season that this place was inhabited, and they are
long gone. You are reminded of your utter solitude, and
loneliness looms large. No point worrying about it, though,
is there? Just breathe, in and out, repeat etc.

Dejectedly, you pick around the items on the floor, careful
not to cut yourself on the short grass. You realise that
not all the discarded jars have been opened. Perhaps the
campers left in a hurry?

BINGO! You find a pot of cous cous!

There is a sticky, black residue on the jar as you pick it
up; it reminds you of anti-vandal paint. You wipe your hands
on your cloak and clean the pot. Excellent, the jar is still
in date – so you **add cous cous** to your inventory.

Exhibit A

You continue south down the cobbled road. Turn to page 18.

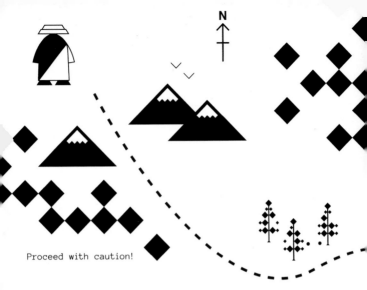

Proceed with caution!

Page sixteen gives you your first real view of
Smorgasboard, and you pause to survey it. The path
heads southeast through a high-sided, desolate gorge.
The terrain here is rather dry – feel the page!

There is little cover, but in the distance, you can
see a group of sparse trees which have etched a living
in this arid region. The land is a black-and-white
monochrome, with hard edges everywhere.

You pass through the valley, footsteps echoing off the
black rock. Pointed hills rise steeply around you. There
is no one to be seen, but you sense that shadowy forces
work against you. Not knowing who to trust, you wonder
if you will ever escape the board...

No point in worrying about it, though. Just breathe.

Approaching the scrubby trees, you realise you haven't relieved yourself for a while and are suddenly desperate. When you've got to go, you've got to go. Go! Grateful for some cover, you nip behind a tree with a paltry collection of sharp, black needles.

As you zip up, you hear a high-pitched, "Pee-pee!" – was it the chattering of birdsong or the giggling of children? You can't be sure. The sound isn't repeated, so you shrug it off and carry on.

As you move out of the trees, a portable toilet cubicle becomes apparent around the corner. A WC for the weary traveller. Alas, you have exposed yourself needlessly.

You proceed, cautiously, as the path curves again to the south and then east. Follow it onwards as the trail carries you over to the next page.

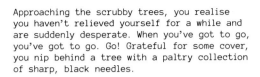

WC

You arrive at a crossroads on page eighteen. A wide, north-south road is cobbled with diamond-shaped bricks and seems to be in good order. Crossing it at a right angle, a smaller track runs east-west. The layout isn't visible on the page; it's in your imagination! Have you read books before? You're picking it up very fast.

You do a little spin to orientate yourself. Always spin clockwise – it just feels right! To the south, the landscape opens up, and you can see the silvery glint of a lake. West, you can see a dry gorge beyond a patch of trees, and to the north, the road disappears into a dark forest about a Smorgometre hence.

To the east, the track runs into tall vegetation just a few steps away. This is smorgrass, similar to grass from your own world, but razor sharp and colourless. The glassy blades bend light; you can see through an individual plant but looking into the meadow is like staring into layers of crystal – distorted and opaque.

There is a Smorgasboard nearby. You steel yourself to read it before deciding on your next move.

Board #2
Bing bong!

You can't squeeze blood out of a stone,
but if you squeeze a stone hard enough, you can bleed!

Hugs and smiles!
Yours, Bongo

That's what counts as entertainment in this place. Well, P, lead on!

To head south towards the lake, turn to page 38.
To head north towards the forest, turn to page 19.
To head east into the smorgrass, turn to page 22.

After some time on the road, you come across an old encampment. The remnants of a fire and the litter give it away – people were here! Unfortunately, smorgrass has started to grow over the campsite debris; it seems it was last season that this place was inhabited, and they are long gone. You are reminded of your utter solitude, and loneliness looms large. No point worrying about it, though, is there? Just breathe, in and out, repeat etc.

Dejectedly, you pick around the items on the floor, careful not to cut yourself on the short grass. You realise that not all the discarded cans have been opened. Perhaps the campers left in a hurry?

BINGO! You find a tin of hotdogs!

There is a sticky, black residue on the can as you pick it up; it reminds you of anti-vandal paint. You wipe your hands on your cloak and clean the can. Excellent, the tin is still in date – so you **add hotdogs** to your inventory.

Exhibit B

You continue north up the cobbled road. Turn to page 20.

You arrive at the border of a dark forest.

There is a black barrel on the side of the road; it looks
like an oil drum and is coated in a slick residue. It echoes
when you give it a kick. There is no signpost here, but
someone has painted onto the top of the barrel in large
white lettering.

> DO NOT ENTER FOREST
> LOOSE LEAVES!

You sense innately that this is a warning, but who has
written it? You take a step forward, on the very edge of
the canopy, unsure. You hear what sounds like a nervous
intake of breath all around you – oh, sorry, that was me.

I don't recommend heading this way, P. This is the entrance
to the Smorgaswood! Loose leaves! I don't think whoever
painted that barrel was just warning you about a cup of
tea.

You peer closer and see that the leaves overhead look like
large shards of glass and are, indeed, loose.

I think you'll need some protective equipment to continue
down there. A hard hat? An umbrella? No, you'd be ripped to
shreds if they fell. I'll leave that one to you, as I'm just
a narrator. I defer to your wisdom.

Where next then, oh great reader? You take a gander.

A solid, cobbled road runs north into the trees, or south
towards a distant crossroads. There is also a chequered
path to the east, curving away from the edge of the forest
towards the pale horizon.

To proceed into the Smorgaswood, turn to page 21.
To bear east along the chequered path, turn to page 28.
To kick the drum again, turn to page 58.
To take the cobbled road south, turn to page 15.

These trees of the deep forest look different from the scrubby conifers you have previously encountered. They have large, veined diamond leaves.

"Deciduous!" a teacher shouts from a distant corner of your mind.

Falling leaves – it can't be that bad, can it?

You enter the forest. Immediately, the light diminishes, and you hear a tinkling overhead. Your adjusting eyes struggle to make out the path, but the sturdy cobbles beneath your feet guide you forward.

The wind starts to build, and overhead a chiming rises as the tinkling leaves knock into each other. You see a single glassy leaf detach from the canopy; as big as your opened hand, it smashes into a thousand shards on contact with the stones.

You gulp, wondering why you didn't listen to the narrator. Wasn't I insistent enough? Should I have used a different tone of voice? Oh well, you're stuffed now. I'll soon be describing you in the past tense.

A northerly gust arrives, shaking all the trees of the Smorgaswood. You turn to flee, bounding towards the patch of light, the exit, and safety.

Leaves smashing all around you, your lack of protection becomes painfully apparent. Shards slice through your cloak and into your matter – whatever it is you are made of. It doesn't matter; you are downed. Some armour might help – you could do with finding a knight! Whatever happened to chivalry, eh? It's too late now. Wincing on the floor, you look up as a dozen piercing leaves hurtle towards you.

Any last words? I usually like it when they perish with an,

"ARRGGHHH!!"

See you on page 12.

Tentatively, you push through the swathe of tall grass. The blades part for you but fall back together with a chime once you have passed. The smorgrass seems to have grown towards the east – it has a directional memory, like velvet. After a few steps, you realise that it would be impossible to return the way you have come without being pierced by the blades. You are in a valve!

After some time, you stumble out of the meadow, unharmed, into a small quadrangle lined with white columns. On the tiled floor, you notice that a small length of grass has splintered off. The blade is smoother at the base and tapers towards the tip like a dagger. It fits in the hand nicely, so you tuck it into your cloak should you need an impromptu weapon.

Add grass dagger to your inventory.

In front of you is another grassy meadow which looks like the last. The blades, however, are aligned towards you, and you cannot pass through. A cold northerly breeze flows over the meadows, creating a polyphonic hum as the blades vibrate. North towards the prevailing wind, the pale ground stretches out into a hazy plain. A chequered path leads that way. South, a narrow path heads downhill. In the distance is the glint of a lake.

"Providence, providence!" you hear a voice croak as you look up.

"Oh, hello dear, welcome to the providore. Can I vend you anything?"

Alarmed, you glance around for the owner of the voice, not having seen another living being for some time. The voice, however, is projected from a black box mounted at the top of a Smorgasboard.

"Trade me, trade me! An item for a thing! An item for a thing! Deposit payment in the honesty box!" crows the loudspeaker. A bin sits on the ground, emitting a low throb. You lift the hinged lid, which has a sticky black coating.

Closer, you can feel air moving towards the empty bin – the honesty box has a suction system. To keep people honest, I suppose. After a brief interlude, the recording starts again, "Providence, providence!..."

A menu is listed on the Smorgasboard – do you want to exchange any items? You may only make specific swaps as listed. If you are unsure, consider exploring the board further before sacrificing your precious items, and return here once you have a plan.

If you wish, ~~cross out~~ a payment item from your inventory, and **add a thing** from the selection below:

Trade flumps for spag bol
OR
Trade cous cous for one stone

If you choose to trade: You place your offering into the bin, and it disappears with a 'THOOM!' A few seconds later, a churning noise occurs, and your purchase pops out. **Add it** to your inventory. Read on.

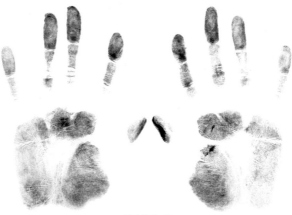

Exhibit C

Before you move on, you read the rest of the Smorgasboard:

Board #3
Bing bong!

The Vending Machine
A play for two actors, by Bongo.

(*A bell chimes as a customer enters the shop.*)

Vendor: Good afternoon, sir.
Customer: Hello, it says outside you're a vending machine shop, but I don't see any vending machines for sale?
Vendor: In a way, we are, sir. You see, vending machines were banned in this country many years ago for being too unreliable and annoying. We have tried to create a truly old-fashioned and authentic vending machine experience.
Customer: Alright then, got any drinks?
Vendor: We represent vending machines, sir. We have many a drink.
Customer: Okay, well, can I just have a bottle of water?
Vendor: I'm sorry, sir, I can't hear you.
Customer: You can't hear me? You just answered me.
Vendor: To order, you must speak in a language I can understand. (*Hands customer a table of codes*)
Customer: What's this?
Vendor: Select the code to get your desired product.
Customer: Really? Okay, bottle of water, erm, D5.
(*No response from Vendor*)
(*Louder*) D5. Bottle of water, please!
Vendor: As I told you. I represent a machine. I can't hear you.
Customer: How do I get my bottle, then? How do you sell anything here?
Vendor: You may enter the product code into this keypad (*hands keypad*).
Customer: Is all this really necessary? Can't I just tell you what I want?
Vendor: (*Annoyed*) Enter the code, or I can't sell anything.
Customer: Fine. D5, oh no, I pressed 4 by mistake.
Vendor: Then you have selected an alternative product! In this case a refreshing zingy can of pineapple and grapefruit crush.
Customer: Does it rhyme with tilt?

Vendor: Other fruit crushes are available.

Customer: So which one is this?

Vendor: Um, well, yes, it rhymes with tilt.

Customer: Okay, fine. How much is that?

Vendor: The product price is displayed on the screen once you have typed in the code.

Customer: I've just typed the code, and I can't see a screen?

Vendor: Yes, unfortunately, the screen is out of order and has been for some time now.

Customer: Well, how much is it then? How much do I pay you for the can!?

Vendor: As the screen is out of order, you must blindly insert money, select the product, and wait for your change. Should there be any change that is. . .

Customer: Fine. Here's smorgpence. Surely, it can't be any more than that for a can of tilt. Where do I. . . do you have a slot?

Vendor: Don't be so revolting, sir. I do not have a slot! You may hand it to me. (Hands him a smorgpenny).

Vendor: Credit one pence. Please select product.

Customer: Again? D4!

Vendor: Two cans?

Customer: No, just one!

Vendor: But you selected D4 twice, sir!

Customer: Because you told me to select it again!

Vendor: Okay.

(Silence)

Customer: Well?

Vendor: Well, what?

Customer: My can of tilt?

Vendor: I am afraid tilt is out of stock, sir.

Customer: Why didn't you say then?!?

Vendor: I'm terribly sorry, sir, but this information is usually displayed on the screen when the product is selected, but as I said, the screen is out of order and has been. . .

Customer: For some time! Yes, you said. Okay, okay.
(Takes a calming breath).
Back to D5 – bottle of water, please. (Inserts D5 into Keypad).

Vendor: Certainly, sir. (Carries bottle over to customer, making electrical noises but stops halfway.)

Customer: Er, thanks. Can I take it now?

Vendor: I am afraid not, sir. Your product is stuck! It hangs there, on the edge of the spiral dispenser, but never falling down. Just out of reach, almost like it's mocking you.

Customer: Great, okay, and there's no way I can get to it, is there?

Vendor: Well, sir, there is one way.

Customer: And what's that?

Vendor: I think you know.

Customer: Er, no, sorry.

Vendor: Shake me.

Customer: Shake you?

Vendor: Yes, sir, shake me! I am a machine that has stolen your money without dispensing the product. Go on, grab me with both hands and give me a shake. Get what's rightfully yours! Only then can we truly say we have given you an authentic vending machine experience. Oh, a simpler time! Shake me, man! Shake me like a robbing machine. Shake me! Shake me!!

Customer: Alright! I'll shake you. (Almost weeping)

(Approaches and starts to gently shake)

Vendor: That's right. Keep going. Harder! Harder! Harder!!

(Vendor starts making high-pitched repetitive noise)

Customer: What are you doing now?!

Vendor: You have set off the alarm, sir!

Customer: This is too weird! Give me my drink, I'm leaving. (Grabs bottle and goes to walk out)

Vendor: You may leave, sir, but you have forgotten one thing!

Customer: What's that?

Vendor: (Wide-eyed) Your change!

Customer: Does it involve more shaking?

Vendor: No sir, all you must do is simply press the appropriate button. . .

(Lifts robe to reveal his navel).

Customer: (Terrified) No, no, NO!! I'm leaving! (Runs out, bell chimes)

Vendor: One day they'll press it, one day. . .

THAT'S CAPITALISM!
Yours, Bongo

Well, that was a long one.

To head north along the chequered path, turn to page 28.
To head south down the narrow lane, turn to page 65.

26

THOOM!

You appear in a narrow, murky ravine, with the sound of running water overhead. Above, the grey light is filtered by a mesh which seems to hold the water aloft. The waterway is smaller here but reminiscent of the Gallery. You notice piles of dark squares, blocks, on either side of the river. The river! Yes, you must be underneath the Smorgastream, which runs into Smorgmere. Those blocks, they look like bricks. You realise that you are almost directly underneath the bridge, now collapsed, that you crossed on entry to Smorgasboard. It would have been easy to observe people crossing the bridge from down here. What is this place, a surveillance post?

Behind you, a large lever is connected to wires which run across the bottom of the ravine and up the sides towards the crumbled structure – a detonator! The plot thickens.

Was the bridge demolition intended to trap you here, or a failed assassination attempt? You shiver at the thought and are keen to get out of here. Quickly, you search the place for anything useful. The only item you can carry is the detonation cord itself. You suppose it could come in useful. You roll up some **cord** and **add it** to your inventory.

Although the north pointer is not visible, you know that the river runs south. Angular shadows flit downstream overhead – migratory fish? You consider following the ravine, but suddenly, a silent pause punctuates the rush of water... Peering around, you spot a few dark specks lying close by in the murk. They shift in the shadows.

Spooked, you return to the Thoomhub. Best not to dawdle. Back into the plumbing, off you pop.

You follow a black and white chequered pavement which slowly curves across the countryside. As you trudge on, you notice the land becomes steadily devoid of features and realise that this path is a sort of borderland with the pure, white wilderness. Hazy light streams overhead and bounces off the pale vastness to the east, straining your sight.

You come across a Smorgasboard at the side of the pavement. Not an obvious junction, you wonder why it would be erected here?

Board #4
Bing bong!

I have released my own perfume called Flanel No.5. And if you fart into a small towel, you can too!

Titters and chuckles!
Yours, Bongo

You pause here, alone, staring out into your future, which looks bleak.

To head east into the tundra, turn to page 29.
To follow the chequered path south, turn to page 33.
To follow the chequered path northwest, turn to page 20.

You turn off the pavement to head onto the tundra, and immediately hear a nearby THOOM! A black dot appears out of nowhere and gradually resolves into a new character closing in on you. A bolshy, cavalier type, bearing a shield and a huge lance of smorgrass. His moustache bounces up and down as the smorgasian charges, no, jumps towards you across the pale field.

Puffing, the knight arrives and manages to voice between breaths,

"Whoa there! No! No, you can't come through here! No entry! Boss's orders. It's just blank pages beyond this point, nothing to see here."

You stop, hesitant. He glances at your hat, seems to like it, and beams you a wide smile.

"Hail, traveller! I am Sir Poignée de L'ansa. Can you understand my accent?" he asks. You nod.
"Are you from abroad?" he asks. You shrug. He shrugs.

"Ha! Anyway, some call me Lance, for short. You can too. Do you like mine? My lance? I like it a lot. Do you mind if I stab you, foreigner?"

You shake your head, alarmed.

"No? Just a little pin prick? No? What about a small, glancing blow?" you step back, nervously watching the tip of Lance's enormous pike.

"Ha-ha! Don't worry, I'm just horsing with you. Look at your face! Ha, just horsing!" Lance chuckles to his own jokes, unbalances himself, and nearly skewers you by accident.

"Oh, ho-ho, watch out there! Ha!"

Your nerves are on edge! Try to relax, P. Inhale slowly, deeply, through your nose. Hold it... One... Two...
And release the air out through your mouth.
Now get a grip. I'm a narrator, not a therapist.

"Whoa! Did you feel that gust? I've spent my whole career galloping around this board, and the tundra still surprises me. Anything could happen! Or nothing."

Lance coughs, "Mostly nothing. Mmph. Just blank pages of course, white as far as the horizon, nothing to see."

You stare beyond Sir Poignée into the pale, hazy distance. He regains your attention by planting himself firmly in front of you, shield pressed close.

"So, P is your name, is it? Well, I'm the guardian of the gateway! This is the door to the tundra, so I suppose you could say I'm its handle, so to speak. Ha! But you can't turn me! No entry!"

Your awkward silence is confused for attentiveness and encourages Lance to start telling you about his old army days, which you perceive to be a hobby of his.

"We used to have a full platoon guarding this checkpoint if you can believe it. Nowadays, we just can't get the staff! Ha!" his moustache jiggles with office humour.

"Just horsing. No, Sir, this was an important posting! I know it looks plain now, you wouldn't have noticed it if you hadn't stepped off the path, but we used to have an actual gateway to defend, very nice, shiny. Lots of polishing. It was a nice living: monitoring, polishing, counting who comes and goes, chatting about polishing and what have you. Now, since the, err, invasion, it's just me left – and nothing to polish! I can count you, though, although you can't come in. I'll add you to a different tally, 'Passers-by reconnaissance.' Tick!" the old soldier reports.

"I can count you, P, but can I count on you? You seem like a good sport, a bit jumpy, perhaps. Are you sure I can't stab you? Oh, jolly well, ha-ha. You don't look like them at the very least..." his voice drops, and he scans the vicinity with suspicion.

Whiskers whispering, Sir Poignée brings you close,

"Do you know what's happened to Smorgasboard, P?" you shake your head in the negatory, and your hat follows suit.

"It's a reign of terror. The board may seem to be devoid of life, but it's quite the opposite. You see, the inhabitants have been displaced." Lance hints, tapping his nose. Or should I say his moustache tip, acting as a finger, taps the middle of his shield, where a nose would be, if he had one.

"It's those blasted marauders! We're hiding from them for the time being. We've been forced underground; not much choice about it, I'm afraid. Dreadful creatures, they hiss, they honk! And worse — there are rumours they are trying to multiply. Have you heard of X? A heinous notion.

"I'm one of the few old warriors that remains to stand up to these beasts, but if I'm honest, I don't claim any pride from guarding this border anymore. We used to parade up and down this pavement. Now I just pop out from a hole in the ground over there! Awfully embarrassing."

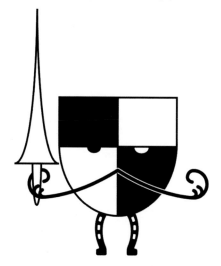

"When they first arrived, we battled hard, oh yes...
Remember to pay your respects at Pagefortytown, won't you?"
Lance sniffs, and a tear runs down his shield.

"We've tried grass daggers, grass spears and grass arrows;
nothing pierces them! I'm sure there must be a way of
beating them – any thoughts? I suppose the trick is in
turning to the correct page."

A grumble emanates from Sir Poignée's innards.

"I say, P, can I ask you a favour? An army marches on its
stomach as they say, ha! You don't, err, happen to have any
pasta tucked away in that cloak of yours, do you? I could
murder a spag bol!"

If you are carrying any spag bol, to give it to Lance, turn
to page 34 now.

If you do not have spag bol, Lance suddenly ducks behind
his shield, shouting,

"Look out! Above!"

Spinning around, you can't see anything in the sky apart
from the north pointer and a distant skein of birds at high
altitude. You are confused by the cause of the knight's
alarm but feel his panic infecting you.

"Flee, good fellow! All speed to you, P. I respect anyone
brave enough to explore the Smorgasboard in these dangerous
times. One last thing – it's not just where you go – it's
how you get there! Direction matters. Now go!" he yells.

Trotting away, you glance over your shoulder to see Lance
cowering under his shield and realise that from above, he
would be nearly perfectly camouflaged with the chequered
path.

To flee south down the chequered path, turn to page 33.
To flee northwest on the chequered path, turn to page 20.

After some time walking through tall grasslands, you stumble out into a small quadrangle with a tiled floor bounded by white columns.

A small black box is mounted at the top of a Smorgasboard, and a large black bin sits on the ground. The place is silent but for the hum of the wind through the grasses.

To the east and west are tall meadows of Smorgrass. They are aligned towards you, and you cannot pass through the blades.

North, a chequered path heads into a hazy plain beyond. South, a narrow lane heads downhill. In the distance is the glint of a lake.

You feel that you are struggling to find what you want, although exactly what this is still eludes you. If only there were someone in charge, an authority figure to whom you could raise your concerns.

Board #5
Bing bong!

Consolidate your moans into one monthly payment!

Complain now.

Call: 0800-978-0-904327-35-9

Love and giggles!
Yours, Bongo

You wonder if there is some sort of code hidden in Smorgasboard, a cipher of letters and numbers whose meaning must be decrypted.

To head north along the chequered path, turn to page 28.
To head south down the grassy lane, turn to page 65.

"Haha! Oh-ho, you are a good sport. Very kind. It's hungry work cantering around, you know!"

Sir Poignee exclaims, grabbing the spag bol off you, which quickly disappears underneath his moustache. ~~Cross spag bol~~ out from your inventory.

"How can I repay you? Let me give you a tip from one adventurer to another. You can spend a lifetime wandering around the upper board, but there's a whole other world beneath our feet you know! It's locked, though, a secret route; you need to know the code to access the mines. I know a chap, Knuckruck, wears a hard hat – he's the key to getting in. I forget his address, but if you can find him, then you'll need to add his page number to another number – I can't remember what, though. The trick is to use the ISBN, the International Standard Book Number. You probably passed it on your way here. You have to average it somehow. Arithmetic was never my forte!

"Anyway, ask around; when you find Knuckruck, add his page number to the ISBN average, then turn to that page and hey presto, you'll find your way underground. Be wary; the enemy sends patrols down there frequently! The Baron is intent on searching us out."

Lance's old army reflexes kick in, and he starts waving you on from the checkpoint. He winks and gives you a final tip before sending you on your way,

"Remember, old chum, that someone is always watching you. Boss's orders, I can't say anymore – all will be revealed!"

To head south down the chequered path, turn to page 33.
To follow the chequered path northwest, turn to page 20.

You enter a large building through dilapidated double doors.
A Smorgasboard stands in the lobby, displaying the script
for the next big production, although there are no actors
to play it and no audience to feign interest.

Board #6
Bing bong!

The Ruler
A one-man show, by Bongo.

(Scene: A low-quality theatre or back room of pub. The audience
is half missing. Of the half present, some have been coerced into
attending. Lighting: Four cheap disco lights cast a warm wash
over the stage. They can flash on activation by sound, although
this mode is not selected. A popular patriotic song plays loudly as
a man enters wearing military ceremonial dress. Enter The Ruler.)

(He strides around the stage, measuring the lengths of arbitrary
distances. He appears unhinged. His uniform is adorned by myriad
rulers hanging off his breast and back, attached using treasury
tags. They rattle loosely. His epaulettes are smaller rulers.
Six tape measures are clipped on o his belt. He stops at the
microphone and measures it.)

(He advances into the audience, traversing the fourth wall
with ease, and hands out the ends of each tape measure to a
member of the audience. They hold him by the waist at a range
of distances e.g. 2cm, 4sm, 7m.)

The Ruler: (Orating) What is the measure of a man!?

What are his dimensions? Length, widtthh, deptttthhh?
Is he tall? Is he short? What shape is he? Is he broad or thin?

Is he square at the shoulder and narrow at the hip? Is he a
rhombus? What is the distance between a man's knees? What is
the area under his curve?

How much courage does he have? 2mm, hmm? 16sm? 30 furlongs?!

I am The Ruler, and today we attempt to measure a man.
But first, retract!

(Audience members release ends of tape measures, which shoot
towards The Ruler. He orates loudly and directly to audience).

A man's wingspan is equal to his height – observe!
(Measures his own height compared to width of outstretched arms.)

180cm – just as I suspected! Did you know that the length of a
man's foot is equal to that of his forearm, or cubit, an ancient
unit of length? Observe!

(Grips own forearm, proceeds to measure this, and length of foot.)
23cm – predictable!

The depth of a man's lunge is equal to the height from the floor to
his knee. Observe!

(Lunges, measures.) 8cm!

The circumference of a man's torso is proportional to the amount
of cheese and meat and cous cous and cake that he gobbles
down from the Smorgasboard! (Measures around the gut.)
The reeeach of a man's tongue (measures this) is equivalent to the
lies and untruths, and deceptions that he has told!

They say you can judge the character of a man not by how he
treats his equals but by how he treats his inferiors. In the Baron's
case, this is difficult to assess because when you ask worms how
they've been treated, you don't get much of an answer.

(Screaming) What is the measure of a man. . . How does he rule?

(Lights down, applause, Bongo bows, ovation. Exeunt.)

Hmm, experimental theatre. You leave the empty box office
and go out onto the street. To your left, the road runs
into some overgrown smorgrass. It is aligned towards you
and would be too dangerous to enter. You head west into the
centre of town. Turn to page 40.

THOOM!

You have arrived at a space outside worlds.

Only one route arrives here, and none leave.

This space is dedicated to Sophie, the author's biggest fan, and to Rosanna, their wonderful daughter.

If you find yourself here, you are welcome to reflect on your own loved ones.

To escape, return to the Thoomhub — if you can remember where it is.

Otherwise, you're stuck.

It's a nice place to be trapped, though!

Walking south, the paved road takes you gently downhill and affords you a view over the board. The main feature in the distance is a lake, with numerous reed beds and an island in the eastern portion. A river curves away to your right – it's the one you crossed on page seven! Widening, its mouth enters the lake at the western edge and cradles a town which has revealed itself at the bottom of the hill. Square-edged buildings with lots of chimneys but no smoke. On the far outskirts of the town, there is a disused power plant. Beyond, there looks to be a short beach at the water's edge.

A silent skein of birds passes high overhead as you enter the town cautiously. You pass the eerie, square houses, stopping at a wonky one that catches your attention. The house is leaning to the right. Craning your neck, you read an inscription on a plaque next to the front door;

Here lived the author, a rhombus enthusiast.

Black and white zebra crossings are in situ at the main intersection, although there are no pedestrians to use them and no vehicles to run them down. A Smorgasboard stands next to the crossing.

Board #7
Bing bong!

A Different Liz
A comedy short, by Bongo.

Traversing a zebra crossing, I saw the rear of someone whom I thought was a Liz that I knew.

"Alright, Liz!" I said.
As the woman pivoted, I realised it was not the Liz that I knew, as I had thought.

"Hi?" she said.
"Oh, sorry, I thought you were someone I knew."
"But I'm Liz. Do I know you?"

"Oh, no, I don't think so. I thought you looked like a Liz that I know, from behind."

"But I am Liz."

"Are you?"

"Yes! Do I know you?"

"No, I don't think so. You're not the Liz that I know that I thought you were, from behind."

"Are you sure? You look sort of familiar?"

"Do I? From behind?"

"No, from the front."

"Oh, but I don't think I know you. No, you're not the Liz that I want."

"Were you looking for Liz?"

"Oh, er no, but I mean, I thought you were someone called Liz that I know, someone called Liz. Not you. Another one. A Liz that I know. I thought I had bumped into her, from behind."

"But not me."

"No. You must be a different Liz."

"Am I not good enough for you?"

"I didn't say that. It's just you're not the Liz that I thought I you were. I mean, the Liz that I know, the one that I thought was you, from behind. But you're not. You're a different Liz."

"Well, I hope you find this Liz. The one that you thought I was."

"Oh, well, thanks, but I don't know her that well, actually. Not well enough to seek her out. Well enough to say hello but not well enough to actively find."

"Obviously not well enough to recognise her! From behind."

"No, not from behind."

Then we parted ways as the queue of traffic became more irate and the honking increased.

Welcome to Pagefortytown!
Yours, Bongo

39

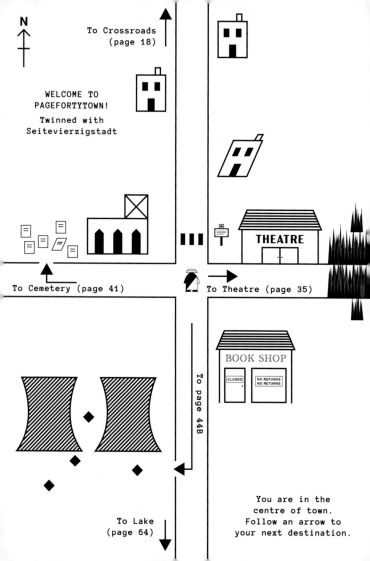

N

To Crossroads
(page 18)

WELCOME TO
PAGEFORTYTOWN!
Twinned with
Seitevierzigstadt

THEATRE

To Cemetery (page 41)

To Theatre (page 35)

BOOK SHOP

CLOSED

NO REFUNDS
NO RETURNS

To page 44B

To Lake
(page 64)

You are in the
centre of town.
Follow an arrow to
your next destination.

You enter a small cemetery to the west of the town. It seems slightly more cheery than the town itself. Most of the gravestones are dark, grey, square slabs with inscriptions memorialising their owners; you notice that a significant portion of the dates of passing are very recent. What happened here?

A wonky gravestone stands out to you in the far corner. Wandering over, you lean your head to the right to read the inscription, realising that this stone isn't wonky - it's a rhombus!

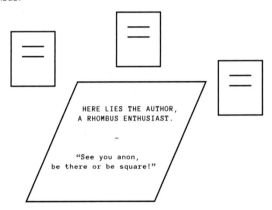

HERE LIES THE AUTHOR,
A RHOMBUS ENTHUSIAST.

-

"See you anon,
be there or be square!"

You meander towards the exit, quietly paying your respects. You notice a freshly disturbed space, although the ground has barely been excavated. To the side lies a small spoon, discarded. It is covered in dirt - the digging tool? Is someone here!?

You suddenly freeze as you hear shuffling behind the nearest headstone. You detect breath sounds, like the passage of air through two nostrils at the end of a very long snout.

To RUN back to the town, turn to page 40.
To confront the creature behind the grave, turn to page 42.

Two small paws grasp the edge of the stone, and slowly, a creature appears over the top of the monument. A nice hat, possibly a beret, creeps into view and is followed by a forehead, some eyes and a large snout which sniffs towards your cloak pockets. The creature seems shy and remains partially hidden.

"Oh hello, hum ho, who are you hoo? Have you come to mourn? That's very kind of you, oh hum. I shall join you, of course. My name is Bishroy. It was my duty to be chief mourner, you know, before the war, oh hum. Many more to mourn now. I am glad of your help. Let us try to dissolve the sorrow with tears, hum ho."

You stand in silence as Bishroy weeps. If you wish to join him, aim your tears here:

"Oh hum, oh dear, the dead. To be buried forever, hum ho. Did you know..." he looks around secretively, "I'm pretending to be dead too!" Bishroy says, changing his tune with a wink.

"They don't come looking for you if you're known to be dead, oh no! I have been trying to dig my own grave as you see here, hum ho, a fine hiding place! But digging is hard, oh hum. They confiscated my spade, and *that* is an inferior spoon." he says, pointing to the little utensil.

"Do you, perhaps, have a big spoon?" he asks, sniffing towards your inventory.

If you have a big spoon, ~~cross it out~~ and turn to page 46.
If you do not have a big spoon, turn to page 44.

"Wot, no big spoon?" Bishroy moans. "Hum ho, no use, oh no."

"Well, don't tell anyone you've seen me. I wasn't here!"

Bishroy flops bodily onto his shallow grave with an audible,

"Pleh!"

His tongue lolls out from under his snout, and he lies motionless.

Surprised by this capricious character and unsure what to do, you observe him for a minute but cannot detect any breathing. You prod him with your foot, his head raises a fraction, and one eye opens just to check who it is, but then he flops back to the ground with another,

"Pleh!"

After this, you can elicit no response whatsoever from this odd Smorgasian. He appears, despite strong motivation, to be completely immobile and perhaps deceased.

You turn back towards town on page 40.

———————————◆———————————

44B

You arrive at an incredible power plant, amazing. This clearly used to be a busy factory, but it has been abandoned. Can you believe it? Two enormously vast, hyperbolic cooling towers rise into the sky. In stark contrast to the squareness of the board, these awesome cylinders curve, narrowing splendidly in the middle. Brutalist architecture at its finest. A few scattered, black shapes litter the ground. You wonder what they are for.

There is no one around. It is eerily quiet.

Return to town on page 40.

THOOM!

You appear amongst several large birds' nests. Shingle
shifts underfoot as you move to peer into the nearest.
Expecting to find shiny white ovals, you are surprised
to discover a sloppy, yellow mush covering the bottom of
the nest. The splash of colour in this monochrome world
intrigues you, so you climb into the nest to investigate. It
still feels warm.

Suddenly, a chorus of alarm calls erupts everywhere,
"HONK! HONK! HONK!"

You look around in panic, realising that you are in the
very centre of Goose Island itself! A heap of black material
towers above you, its base close by. Long necks rear up all
around, a gaggle of beady eyes trained on you.

In the sky, the silhouette of an angry mother appears from
the shadow of the tower, angling this way. This yellow mush
is what she has been incubating, and you are in the middle
of her nest!

You look around for the tube entrance. While searching,
you realise that all of these confused, broody geese are
sitting on the same yellow mush. Scrambling to your feet,
realisation suddenly hits you. Scrambled! They're laying
scrambled sgeg!

You have no time to scavenge for items, quick P, back
through the portal! Mother goose dives towards you, but you
escape by turning back to the Thoomhub just in time.

```
                         Z                    Z
          Z              x                    x
          x                        Z
                  V                 x                    Z
                         P                    x
  Z                      x
  x              Z                    Z
                 x                    x
```

You hand the big spoon to Bishroy, who snaffles it from you, delighted. Eager to get digging, he emerges from behind the gravestone and gives you a warm hug.

"Oh! How can I repay you, dear traveller? Hmm ho? Would you like to go underground too? That's not a death threat, oh hum, oh no. Let me impart a secret of sorts.

"You can travel the board very quickly underground, you know, in the tunnels, oh yes! If you see a black barrel, give it a kick twice, oh yes. But not three times! Oh hum, oh no. I forget where it is...

"There's an old friend of mine, chief of something or other, he's a bit of a square, but he loves digging too. If you see him, use the code! The mode of the code! The mode of the code, oh hum, oh sum..."

Bishroy hums to himself, turning towards his grave to be.

"Farewell, hum ho. Please don't tell anyone you've seen me. I wasn't here!"

Bishroy begins hacking at the earth with his new tool, seemingly no longer aware of your presence.

You turn back towards town on page 40.

You arrive on a short, white, sandy beach. Across the shimmering lake is a shingle island with some trees. You have the vista to yourself. The river mouth to your right babbles pleasantly over some rocks, and you enjoy the sound for a moment.

Concentrate, P. Bongo's survival depends on you! Do you ever want to get out of here? Reading on begrudgingly, you observe a short pier jutting out into the water. A rowing boat is moored there. Two paths lead away from the beach: the main road northwest towards a town, the other a narrow lane northeast through a grassy meadow. A Smorgasboard stands at the near end of the jetty.

Board #8
Bing bong!

Scratch and sniff – the aromas of Smorgasboard!

1. The carcass of a tree

2. Fibrous cellulose pulp

3. Thin sheet material

4. Ink display medium

Keep smelling!
Yours, Bongo

To walk out onto the jetty, turn to page 48.
To swim into the lake, turn to page 52.
Take the road northwest via page 64, or follow the grassy lane northeast on page 65.

You stroll down the jetty to take a closer look at the rowing boat and are taken aback to discover an attractive female form reclining in the bottom of the vessel. You realise a pretty Smorgasian is hiding here and sunbathing at the same time. Her slender figure is rather obvious through an expensive dress, so you avert your eyes and politely cough to announce your presence.

"Oh, who's this, another peeper?" she giggles.
"You can look, you know. I don't mind." she intones, smiling at you.

"I'm Conqutie – but you probably knew that already didn't you. Have we met before? I don't remember. Love your cloak, by the way x." she says, looking you up and down. Whilst holding a smile, she winces a touch as she spots your feet.

"Have you been traipsing around looking for me? I don't mind fans, but I'm not interested in another stalker, thank you!" she sighs.

"Look, you'd better come in, or they'll spot you." Conqutie beckons you into the boat, which rocks as you enter it to lie next to her. You squeeze yourself in amongst oars.

"Comfortable? What do you think of Bongo? Did you read that Smorgas on the board over there? Hee-hee. I like him. He's always got fresh content."

Embarrassed, you lie in the bottom of the hull as she presses up to you. Her geometry is perfect. You turn to face away, unsure of her intentions.

"Rude. I'm thinking about getting my own narrator. It's nice to control what people think about you, isn't it? But yours is right, I am very beautiful. The top half, at least. My legs are so short, and I hate my feet. Ugh, they are like hooves! So out of fashion, just like yours. Oh, sorry."

She pulls you close from behind; you can feel her breath on your cheek. Your heart hammers; this relationship has moved so fast. You realise that you are already spooning – and that you are the inferior spoon!

"Can I ask you something, dear... Do you have any hotdogs?" she whispers seductively.

"I would so love to fax my friends showing off some nice long legs on the beach. I'll give you something in return, this, one of my most prized possessions – a mirror."

Conqutie pulls out a big spoon from amongst her frock.

"Smorgmere is so shiny anyway, the lake that is – I can always use that. Oh, please give them to me. Have I influenced you? :P x"

If you have hotdogs, ~~cross them out~~ and turn to page 50 now.

If you have "No hotdogs!?" Conqutie sighs and rolls her eyes. Annoyed, she tips you into the Smorgmere, and a current from the nearby river carries you out, away from the jetty. The fickle Smorgasian lies back in the boat without a second glance.

Turn to page 52.

Pleased, Conqutie grabs the tin, shoving it into the depths of her gown. She throws the big spoon into your lap.

"New legs! Oh, thank you, so kind! You're really brave, wandering around like there's no war on. You could get picked off at any minute if they fly over! They're over there, you know, on the island."

You turn to face her, wondering what she is talking about, and she leans in close. You wonder if she is about to kiss you, but instead, she hisses,

"The GEESE!!" and stands up suddenly.

The craft rocks dangerously as Conqutie gives you a final smile and laughs, "Bye! x"

She leaps overboard with a splash, splattering you with silvery droplets. Alarmed, you peer over the gunwale but can only see your own reflection. You try to stare into the depths after her, but the lake has the most mirror-like surface you have ever seen. Your eyes swim dreamily in the shimmering surface...

You awake at the bottom of the rowing boat to find yourself caressing and kissing an oar, which is covered in an inky residue – are there squid in this lake?

Longingly, you gaze into your upside-down image in the concave surface of the spoon, wishing it was another set of eyes looking back at you.

Exhibit D

Come on, P, stop daydreaming! You seem overly fond of that oar. **Add that big spoon** to your inventory, and let's go.

To return to the beach, turn to page 47.
To row out into the lake, turn to page 53.

You are floating in the middle of Smorgmere, the silver, mirror-like lake that dominates the southern board. To the west is the river mouth, to the north a beach, and to the east an island. South, the shore is very distant, and you don't feel particularly buoyant. The water has washed you clean, including all that brick dust – nice to feel fresh! Cross out brick dust from your inventory.

It's not bad here, is it, drifting? We can hang around on this page for a while if you fancy. If you don't read on, at least nothing bad can happen to you. Start again from the top if you like; bask in the words. I liked 'buoyant'. Bobbing around like a cork, it's easy to get lost in the reflection of the water...

Oh no, what's happened now!? You've got us flipped in the mirror lake! I must say I have had some incompetent readers in my time, but you are on another level. Unreadable text, perfect. I assume you know how to resolve this P. Otherwise, we're stuck. I'll just wait. You're on your own time now.

As you reflect on your conundrum, you notice ripples approaching you across the shimmering water. Four shadows encircle you, hiding just beneath the surface, a shoal! You feel a fin slide across your feet as you tread water. What's the meaning of this? Suddenly, a splash erupts as a distressed fish leaps out of the water before falling back into the mere, then bobs up next to you, injured. It floats on its side with fishing line protruding from its mouth. It is an angular shape with four even sides and silvery scales. An unfamiliar species to you but common in this region, the others continue to circle at a distance; they seem to want your help. You empathise with the squalmon but fear that whoever bait this was, it has been swallowed hook, line, and sinker. The lure has been taken down, and the fate of this fish looks grim. Sadly, you decide to put it out of its misery with a swift bonk to the head. It slowly sinks, and the ripples of its shoal mates fade away.

If you want to progress:

To swim towards the beach, flip to page 47.
To swim towards the island, flip to page 79.

Clumsily you assemble the oars into their locks and row out from the jetty. At best, you are an amateur rower, but even so, you find it surprisingly difficult to make headway. The boat spins one way, seemingly pushed by the current from the river mouth, but then spins the other, perhaps due to the northerly wind. You try your best to hold the skiff in a straight line but cannot progress more than a few boat lengths before losing control. The more energy you exert, the stronger the currents seem to become.

Eventually, you find yourself in the middle of the lake. From here you can see a heap of black material piled high in the centre of the island. However, unfathomable forces work against you every time you row towards it.

You concede defeat and lie back on the seats of the boat. Thwarted, you drift with the currents of Smorgmere and think of Conqutie. Clouds pass overhead, forming shapes in your mind. Smooth outlines, alluring curves. Then, oh gosh, please stop now, P. I can't describe that.

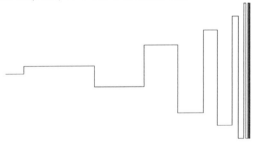

You feel a gentle swell lapping, and the boat begins to rock with the larger surf as you approach the shore. Riding the crest of a wave, you feel the friction of shingle against the hull as you wash up on the beach, less than a stone's throw from the jetty, whence you came.

You discover a length of knotted fishing line washed up at the high water mark. What a tangled yarn! You coil it up and **add line** to your inventory. Turn to page 47.

You balance atop your makeshift vessel. Hollow, black canes, they are quite stiff and should support your weight until the author deemed otherwise, may he rest in peace. You use the longest reed to push away into the flow of the river and glide downstream. Now you really are a punter, P!

Just as you are perfecting your boatmanship, the river splits into several channels. You notice the banks here are lined by tufts of smorgrass. Suddenly,

THOOM, THOOM, THOOM!

You hear both riverbanks explode with noise and glimpse dark, distorted shapes moving amongst the foliage. As you approach the labyrinth of rivulets, a volley of arrows is released towards you from both sides! These are grass darts and will easily pierce you.

Navigate your way downstream, avoiding the missiles.

Exhausted from your ordeal, you collapse on the raft. An arrow has landed so close to you that your cloak has been pinned – the missile still projects from the reeds. You remove it and **add grass dart** to your inventory.

A familiar, glittery tingle hits you as a northerly breeze blows across the ends of the reeds, playing a tune that lulls you to sleep...

Bongo comes into sight, and what a miserable sight. The jester lies sprawled on the floor of his cell as if he has just endured terrible punishment. He twitches, feeling your presence in the shared dream, and shakes himself awake before pleading to you in earnest. In person, he seems much less jolly than his comedy suggests. This time the vision has audio.

Adventurer!
Oh, please help! Not just for myself, although I would be very grateful to be rescued . . . but I fear the Baron is hatching a plan against the whole of Smorgasbord itself! The land is empty, and the people hide in fear, terrorised by the Baron's thugs. Somehow he lured them here and, by a trail of breadcrumbs, led them across the bridge and then south to the island. He commands their obedience, I am not sure how. I fear that in order to get to the castle, you will have to defeat them first. Good luck!

As you can see, the sprite has agreed to help me reach out to you once more, although doing so, she puts herself at great risk. Her home is an enclave in the woods, a leafy independent zone. It is a secluded place devoid of visitors. I'm afraid I can't be more specific. Time is short – if you seek her out, she can help us. I forget her name, perhaps Lily, or Lucy, or Lola.

One last thing – the island! If in doubt, swim!

You awake to find yourself drifting through the river mouth as it emerges into a wide lake. Alongside the raft, a packet of flumps is floating, which you pluck out of the water. **Add flumps** to your inventory. As you drift further into the lake, your trusty reed raft slowly disintegrates and leaves you treading water. Turn to page 52.

Typically, against advice, you swing onto the bank and head west into the thorny overgrowth that is undoubtedly a dead end. Wasting everyone's time, you find that the thorns have become overgrown, and the path narrows ahead. Please turn back, P. This path is even further west than page one; if you're not careful, we'll stray into the prequel.

Finally, predictably, the thorns are so thick that you cannot progress. There is a tiny window of light through the dense spikes, and you catch a peek of another land, but that is described separately. A bright bow has been caught on the thorns. Perhaps that girl did pass through here after all. No such luck for you.

Did you not understand cul-de-sac?

Swallowing your pride, you give up and return the way you came. Ha! Knew it. As the path opens up, the river reappears. You leap onto the ribbon-rope and shimmy down onto the raft of reeds.

Turn to page 54.

You kick the black drum a second time, and the noise resounds internally. This time, however, the lid pops off and is followed by a very angry individual who erupts from the barrel with an ominous glare, which is aimed at you.

"Oi! Who do you think you are? I've had just about enough of people kicking my barrel, and YOU have done it twice in as many minutes. See this rock? This is made of the hardest rock which has ever been mined under Smorgasboard, and I've a mind to headbutt you with it!"

The gruff Smorgasian points to a shiny black helmet which obscures all his facial features apart from a tight-lipped mouth. The helmet has upside-down crenellations and looks extremely uncomfortable, but, you agree, very solid.

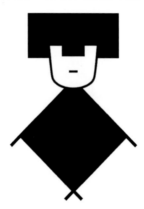

"You can't come in. Now get lost!"

He leaps back into the barrel and slams the lid shut.

To kick the drum again, turn to page 75.
To proceed into the Smorgaswood, turn to page 21.
To bear east along the chequered path, turn to page 28.
To take the cobbled road south, turn to page 15.

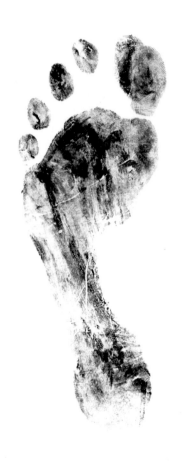

Exhibit E

The cobbled road heads downhill as you approach the beach. The water is silvery and inviting. You are tempted to throw off your cloak and dash into the water, but please, resist. Swimming alone can be dangerous. As the road blends into the white sand, another Smorgasboard looms at you with some irrelevant poetry. Rather obscure these 'clues', aren't they? I wouldn't bother.

Board #9
Bing bong!

Spag Bol
A poem by Bongo.

Bring a meaty spag,
Spag bol, meaty bol.
A mushroom spag,
Much room for bol.
A bowl of bol, a bowl, a bol,
Spag bol alongside alcohol.
Bring a bottle to pop - red wine unplugged,
Get off, it's mine! Red wine is glugged.
Spag boLogin @www.spagbol.net,
Spag bol may be bettered by a buttered baguette.
Chuck some onion in the bol and
GIVE IT A STIR.
Check the flavour's never bland,
Black pepper, Sir?
I'm a spag bol fan straight from the pan,
Last thing, sprinkle Parmesan.
Spoon and fork, twirling pasta for days,
Spaghetti spag spag spag spag bolognese!

It's me verses you!
Yours, Bongo

Turn to page 47.

The trail is steeper than you thought and rather muddy! You plant a foot which sinks into the sludge. Retracting the limb, you tip ungracefully onto your back. Before you know it, you are sliding down the riverbank, and it's too late to turn around! You are in a valve.

Exhibit F

The black slime cakes your cloak, and your efforts to gain purchase are in vain. Your speed increases down the mudslide, straight towards the ravine!

You glance around in desperation, flailing wildly. Look, P! Suspended over the ravine to your left, is it a rope? It's your only hope. If you launch yourself just before the edge, you could grab it. Unfortunately, your trajectory is well off. Quick, tilt the book to the left now!

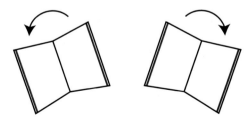

Too far! Back to the right! That's better. Now jump! Reach!

Phew. You manage to grab the rope and realise that it is more of a ribbon – how did this get here..? It must be a type of bookmark left behind by one of your predecessors. Yes, I think I remember her now. Nice girl. Had a bow tied around her hat. It had a lovely wide brim, too, just like yours. She was a clever one if I remember rightly; she saw through the Baron's trap straight away – didn't even cross the bridge on page six! She abseiled straight off the bottom of the page – must have used this ribbon, I suppose. I didn't narrate her after that. I wonder where she ended up...

Anyway, you're dangling on the end of a line above a raging torrent, P! It's not a good look. On the far bank, a small track leads into tangled undergrowth. You can probably swing there. However, a Smorgasboard at the start of the path says:

Board #10
Bing bong!

Cul-de-sac, cul-de-sac.
Don't go down the track, you'll have to turn back.

Rhymes!
Yours across the board, Bongo

The finest poet in all of Smorgasboard he is. That might be the first one that's actually useful, though. For once, I agree with the clown.

To the north, the river is flowing towards you, impassable. To the east is the slope you slipped down; it's a no-go. However, below you, there does appear to be a loose mat of reeds floating in an eddy on the river – ever tried rafting?

To swing west and leave the riverbank, turn to page 57.
To drop onto the mat of reeds, turn to page 54.

The tunnel guardian tenses and growls at you. He looks mean.

"Wrong page number! Why don't you have the correct code?"

You freeze, unsure what you have done wrong. The gruff fellow advances, interrogating you,

"Are you a spy? Have you been sent by Baron Smorg to infiltrate us?"

Nervous, you can do little more than mumble incoherently, your floppy hat trembling.

"What was that? A low grumble? Or was it a mumble? It doesn't matter either way – you need to learn a thing or two about averages!" the helmeted barrel dweller spits.

"What's your purpose here, stranger – to get to the castle? You think you can escape there, do you? Mmph. Well, there is more than one way to get there, but you won't be coming this way – not today! Not past Knuckruck!"

The hard-headed Smorgasian strikes the drum. A resounding note tolls across the landscape.

"I give you to the count of zero, stranger. Run!" he yells murderously.

You turn heel and begin to flee south down the paved road. Your trapezoid feet clatter away at the cobbles. You hear the barrel tolling again, with Knuckruck, bizarrely, counting out loud,

"Zero–zero–zero!"

The tolling ceases, and you risk a glance back. The tunnel guardian shouts, "It tolls for thee!"

Knuckruck makes an inhuman dive, headfirst across the span between you. You are crushed and killed by his crenelated cap. Turn to page 12.

Trudging along the lonely road, you spot a small trail to the west down a steep slope. You glimpse water flowing in the gully. It's the river from page seven again, running south to the lake!

A Smorgasboard stands nearby.

Board #11
Bing bong!

Being the 'big spoon' or the 'little spoon' is actually a misnomer. Spoons of the exact same size fit together perfectly, as demonstrated here.

Dollops of fun!
Yours, Bongo

To the north lies a settlement.

Your choices are black-and-white:

To turn off down the western slope, turn to page 61.
To plod north into the town, turn to page 40.
Page 60 will take you south to the beach.

Journeying along the lane, pleased you have survived thus far, you feel a bound in your step. Literally – the ground suddenly gives way underfoot. Your reflexes sharp as smorgrass, you recover without fully embarrassing yourself and quickly realise that you have stumbled onto what appears to be a large trampoline embedded in the floor.

After crawling to the middle like a juvenile, you begin bouncing on the rubbery, black surface. Boing, boing! Getting higher – hold onto your hat! Boing! So high now, you can see above the smorgrass meadows. Boing! To the south, you glimpse a silvery lake; it looks like the lane takes you down to a beach that way. You spin clockwise as you jump – boing! Just beyond the smorgrass to the west, there is a modest town – civilisation! It doesn't look to be far through the meadow. You rotate before you can study the settlement any further. Boing! To the north, a grassy lane runs uphill towards some distant white columns. Boing! East, beyond the grassland, is a strange white plain, hazy to the horizon. You can't see a route that way, though.

Panting, you decide your next step:
To head south, turn to page 47.
To head west, turn to page 66.
To head north, turn to page 33.

You stumble out of the glassy meadow to find yourself on the fringes of a sleepy settlement. You wonder where the inhabitants are. In your opinion, this place feels too quiet. Others may disagree, however; I find silence to be appropriate when people are reading!

Before you continue, you realise a tall shaft of smorgrass has broken off. The pointy end leans toward you threateningly. Grasping the javelin, you spin it around a few times to demonstrate aptitude with this weapon. Not bad – where did you learn that? You slip the weapon through your belt.

Add grass spear to your inventory.

Assessing your surroundings in more detail, it seems like this town has been deserted for some time. The grass behind you has grown across the paving, reclaiming what used to be an open avenue. A large, dilapidated building is close by, set off from the street in front of you. You recognise this as a theatre, mainly due to the word THEATRE emblazoned above the double doors. The wind blows cold from the north once more. Reminded of western films from your own realm, you imagine a whistling tune and, almost on cue, a large feather tumbles across your field of view.

A Smorgasboard stands nearby.

Board #12
Bing bong!

Having a buffet?
Cous cous is an absolute must must!

Tickles!
Yours, Bongo

To enter the theatre, turn to page 35.

To go straight to the centre of the town, turn to page 40.

Taken aback, you issue a thousand apologies, stating you didn't realise he lived in the barrel. You see him calming down and politely enquire of his name.

"Mmph. It's Knuckruck. And I don't live there. My quarters are below, obviously. I'm the tunnel warden and chief mining controller, you know. Guarding the tunnel entrance is the main work we have now that we've stopped digging."

Feeling you have got him on topic, you enquire more about the tunnels.

"Oh, you don't know? Well, of course, we've conducted extensive excavations under the entire board for many years. Black barrels popping up everywhere as air vents! Usually concealed, of course, planning permission and all that. You can use them to get to distant corners of the board very quickly, oh yes, lots of portals! But only one main entrance. This old thing." he gives the metallic drum two knocks.

"Of course, the downside is that it's impossible to tell direction underground, so you could, er, pop out anywhere, so to speak."

He seems pleased that you have taken an interest and invites you down the shaft, which plummets into blackness inside the barrel. Be careful, P. You must always wear a helmet underground. You've got a hat, which is a weak type of helmet, but at least it's something. That's a bit of a grey area, to be honest.

"You might want to take a last look at the daylight!"

Knuckruck says before you follow him down a ladder into the deep.

Down.
Down.
Down.

Read on.

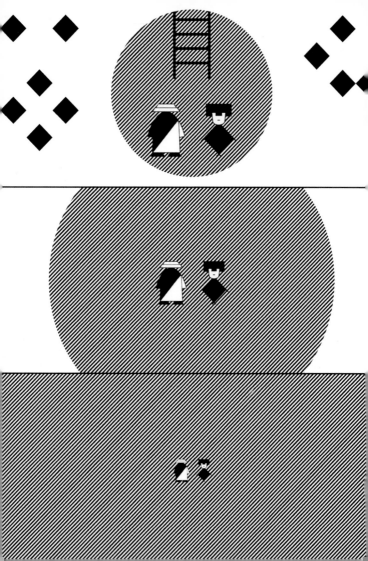

You follow the warden closely along a wide tunnel, which is dimly lit by lanterns suspended from the ceiling every hundred or so paces. Knuckruck isn't much of a talker but leads you with confidence into the gloom. Your route through the mine splits down multiple forks, occasionally backtracking, with nothing but the black walls to follow. You try to remember your way in, but before long, you are hopelessly lost. After what seems like an hour but could be mere minutes, you come to a halt at a dead end. Broken slabs of black rock lie strewn on the floor, reminding you of slate.

"Mmph. This must have been an old mine face. Makes me sad to see it abandoned." Knuckruck pronounces gruffly. You inquire why he has led you here.

"What do you mean?" he replies, "I don't know where we're going either. That's the nature of these caverns; you just have to keep going until you bump into the place you want to be."

Astonished by this lax attitude to subterranean navigation, fears of being lost and perishing in the darkness flood your mind. Knuckruck seems trustworthy, but if it came to it, you suspect he would eat you first. You wonder why the system hasn't been mapped or some sort of guideline network installed. As if he is being narrated simultaneously, Knuckruck responds, "Well, it's not for lack of effort. We did try glowing way markers a while back, but it led to even more deaths than before. You see, the caves randomise themselves. They're constantly changing. New passages open, and old ones collapse. It's a lot like life, I suppose. Look, don't worry, I haven't died yet! We'll probably come across some interesting caverns soon and then some portal spouts."

Not waiting for you to moan anymore, Knuckruck marches off into the dark. You strive to keep up, not wanting to be left behind. Slowly your eyes adjust to the gloom, but you don't gain any benefit from it - it looks the same. Trotting behind the hard-headed mining controller, you follow around countless corners, up a ramp, down some stairs, onto the next line and to the end of another sentence.

You hear a 'click, click, click' reverberate around the tunnel, and realise it is coming from Knuckruck. He stops abruptly, listening for the echo.

"We're here!" he pronounces, "You are in a silo."

Unsure what this Smorgasian is talking about, you also pause but can detect no discernible change in the darkness. You wonder whether there is anything under that helmet.

"Can't you hear it?" he asks. You shake your head, curious.

"Click, click, click!" Knuckruck sends out his glottal sonar once more, probing into the murk, then listens.

"There! You can hear them, or rather, you can't. Flumps!" he beams as you look on incredulously.

"They absorb sound, compared to the hard walls of the mine. We must be in a chamber right underneath the providore. All the donated items from the upper board have to go somewhere for storage; the honesty box is plumbed into the barrel system and the suction carries them down here to be fly tipped." he explains, as if it was obvious.

An unusual system, don't you think, P? It seems strange that someone would offer to trade you spag bol for some flumps but then simply discard them underground. It's almost as if the whole thing was engineered to ensure you travelled around most of the upper board before you were able to access this zone. It sounds like you're not the first victim, either. I suspect the Baron's hand is at play here.

You explore the cavern with Knuckruck; the floor becomes a soft carpet of semolina as you head towards the wall – it's cous cous! Treading over the damp grains, you hear the low thrum of air moving under pressure. You feel a cold jet blow over you from an invisible pipe somewhere above as you arrive, indeed, at a large pile of flumps.

Add flumps to your inventory, again.

At the far side of the chamber, two tunnels lead away into the pitch.

Knuckruck turns to you, saying, "I think we should split up, then between us, we'll have more chance of finding where it is that we want to go. If you find it first, then I'll catch up with you later, but if I find it first, then you can catch up later, and vice versa. It's a win–win. Do you want to go this way or that way?"

The tunnel warden looks impatient, and you eye his helmet warily. There is no time to question his logic.

To go this way, turn to page 72.
To go that way, turn to page 76.

◆

71B

THOOM!

You appear in a marsh, amongst black reeds, with high tufts of smorgrass surrounding you nearby. The sudden noise disturbs a bird from the undergrowth. It honks indignantly as it flaps away. Wading amongst the creeks, you observe muddy imprints crisscrossing the swamp. Footprints, but not like yours. Clearly, many other people were here. You follow the prints to a reed bed, which seems to have been the centre of activity. A broken, black crossbow lies discarded in the reeds. Salvaging what you can, you detach the string from the weapon. **Add string** to your inventory.

You squelch around, frequently getting stuck in the bog, but can find nothing else worth mentioning.

Return to the Thoomhub.

You strike out alone into the blackness. Twisting and turning through cramped passages, you can hear your breath close. You pause to collect yourself before hearing a deep rumble, followed by a tremor that runs through the walls. You freeze as black dust falls from the ceiling — the benefits of a wide-brimmed hat! It must have been a distant tunnel collapse. You gulp, listening hard as the quake fades.

You prepare to press on, but your sharp ears pick up another fainter sound; A pitter-patter of feet coming towards you down the tunnel. It sounds like two pairs.

What was it Sir Poignée de L'ansa said about enemy patrols in the mines? You have an overwhelming sense that the owners of the approaching feet may be unfriendly. You press yourself close to the wall, but how can you hope to avoid them in such a narrow channel?

P   Z Z

You hold your breath whilst pulling yourself as tight to the stone as possible, and the patrolling feet draw close. You detect movement up ahead, followed by a sharp, low "Hisss!!" Have you been spotted!? You reach around in desperation; by chance, your hand catches on a small crack in the stone behind you. Feeling deeper, the crack heads further into the wall!

The fissure is extremely tight, and there are no lanterns to light your way, but what choice do you have...

Total oblivion, or total oblivion?

If you have one stone, you may turn to page 74 now.

If not, your only hope is to get out of this tunnel and hide on an adjacent page. Quick, read on!

You squeeze yourself into the fissure as the slapping of feet rushes towards you. Just in time! Before you are more than an arm's reach into the crack, a malicious hiss erupts in the main passage. Terrified, you push on into the crevice as a beak snaps at thin air behind you. The creature is too bulky to fit down here, and fortunately, you remain paper thin, not having had a bite to eat since your arrival in Smorgasboard. The gap widens in front of you, and you sigh of relief as you escape. The hissing recedes, and your stomach grumbles in triumph.

You realise that you are actually very hungry. You have been exercising a lot after all and could do with a snack. Perhaps a slice of cake, or even better, a finger buffet! You're in the midst of the Smorgasboard, however, and those luxuries aren't just lying around.

You could tuck into those flumps?
You probably won't need them for anything else.

~~Cross out flumps~~ from your inventory and gobble them down.

If you prefer to resist the sweet temptation, you collapse from low blood sugar and immediately perish – turn to page 12.

Ooh, I was a bit coercive there, wasn't I? I'm just looking out for you, P. You need the energy, you look drained.

You continue to explore the subterranean labyrinth:

If you went this way, turn to page 76.
If you went that way, turn to page 80.

Feeling bold, you remove one stone from a pocket and turn
to face the advancing patrol. Heart hammering, you plant
your feet and grip the stone hard, causing you to bleed.
Out of the blackness, two hefty, long-necked birds step
into view. The baron's soldiers – foreign recruits! A single
lantern above illuminates a space for you to duel these
bandits. They have the symbol of Smorg emblazoned on their
breasts and are studying you carefully.

They seem to decide that you are a threat or a wanted
fugitive, lowering their necks aggressively with a
frightening hiss. One nods to the other, and then they rush
towards you, at either side of the tunnel, although there
isn't much room for them to truly flank you. You take aim at
the right-hand goose and throw the stone before fumbling
for your grass weapons to take on the second. To your
disbelief, the stone strikes the first bird hard between the
eyes, then bounces off to hit the left-hand attacker in the
temple.

Chuck! "Honk!", "Honk!"

The stone disappears down the tunnel. ~~Cross it out~~ from
your inventory.

Both geese collapse, sliding towards you along the solid
floor. Feathers askew, they flap, then they snap, then
they are still. That was a fair bit of luck! You pant
hard, adrenaline running high. You have taken a life. Two
lives. And you intentionally chose the path of violence,
interesting. I'm not sure what to make of you now, P.

Guilt-ridden, you hurry away from the site of the battle
along yet more tunnels.

If you went this way, turn to page 76.
If you went that way, turn to page 80.

You have kicked the drum a third time. I am not sure this was a wise move. You shake the pain of the impact out of your trapezoid foot.

The barrel rumbles ominously, and the tunnel guardian bursts out again, even more enraged.

"Who do you think you are, stranger? Do you think you can just kick your way into my domain with those clods of yours? No passcode or anything, just a floppy hat, the arrogance of it!"

You tremble as he approaches and squares up to you, analysing.

"Do I recognise you, mmph? Have you applied for a job with us recently? Hmm. Perhaps not."

He paces around you, rooting you to the spot with a glare.

"You're clearly in a rush to get into my tunnels... that's right, Knuckruck's tunnels! Mine! What do you think your chances of survival are without me down there, mmph? Zero! Zero, I say! Don't believe me? You'll never get to the castle with that attitude!" the Smorgasian lectures you.

You try to edge away from this controlling individual, but he grips you with surprising strength. He shakes his head with a murderous look. You cannot move. He checks you over, then seems to make up his mind about something.

"Farewell, foreigner, down the rabbit hole!"

Knuckruck picks you up forcefully and dumps you into the black barrel. There is a ladder to one side, but you cannot get hold of it. You plummet down a long, dark shaft and land broken on the cold, hard floor.

Turn to page 12.

After another journey through the cramped darkness, you begin to slow down, feeling that the walls on either side of you are widening into a larger space. Perhaps you are developing your own sense of echolocation?

You continue into a strange cavern, and your eyes have to adjust again to a hazy, silver twilight. There are no lanterns here, they aren't needed, and it is difficult for you to judge how far away the ceiling is. Dim, shimmering light penetrates through the cavern roof, the greyness stretching out for as far as the eye can see – this place is vast!

You cannot help but stumble into the cavern, looking up in awe at the enchanting ceiling. You quickly shiver with regret as your trapezoids step into a cold puddle.

'Splish! Splash! Splosh!' You hear echoed around the place as you wade through. Watch out, it's onomatopoeia!

A familiar, mocking voice leers at you from behind a nearby stalagmite,

"Oh, look who it is, the voyeur! Well, you've come to the right place for that."

Conqutie saunters out, her angular shape striking in the twilight.

"So you've got this far; I must admit I didn't think that you would."

You shuffle awkwardly, trying to make your cloak look presentable.

"Heehee!" she giggles, "Do you know where we are?" You shake your head in reply.

"They call this place the Gallery. We use it to keep a watch on them. Take a look, lie down. I wonder if you can work it out. Tell me what you see." Conqutie commands, taking up position on the floor next to you.

Obediently, you study the ceiling — it reminds you of stargazing back home. As you focus, you realise that the light is not uniformly silver. There are patches of shadow and movement to be seen. You struggle to concentrate with Conqutie lying beside you but are keen to impress. There is a large blotch of shadow away to your left, separate from the dark walls of the cavern. Smaller, dark specks move around the big blotch. Closer to hand, on your right, you view another shadow; a rectangle with legs? Beyond this, the ceiling seems to ripple as if it is flowing somehow...

You are hit with epiphany as you realise that you are under the lake! The large blotch is the island, the rectangle with legs must be the jetty, and the small specks — are they geese? Your awe is doubled as you fully appreciate the nature of the Gallery. A whole cavern beneath Smorgmere! But how is the water held up..?

You turn to enquire of Conqutie, confused.

"Heehee. Look at your face! You've got to stop thinking like you're at home, P. Your rules don't apply! This is Smorgasboard, after all: a mixture, a variety, an assemblage, a miscellany, an assortment, a medley! Anything can be found here. Okay, you look like you want an explanation. The water is held up by a semi-permeable membrane, like a fine mesh. The holes are just big enough to admit a smorgasian but too small for water to drip through. Don't ask how — it's like a clever sieve, although we do have one leak — that puddle you splashed through. The Smorgmere is a mirror, as you've seen from above, but it's actually a two-way mirror.

"We can observe what happens on the surface of the lake from this vantage point, which is why it's so valuable. From here, we can monitor the enemy's movements! Or at least know when they set off from their headquarters. It's a useful warning system; when we see them set out from the island, we can warn others to hide. Patrols do come down here, of course, through the tunnels, you've got to be on your toes, but they don't stay for long; they always return to the upper board to roost on the island."

"Ugh, yawn, explaining things is boring! Has your narrator gone on strike or something?" she explains, like a spoilt Smorgasbrat.

"When I swam down from the boat, I was watching your face search for me. Bless. I've been here since – I'm on sentry duty again. It's a nice view, but there's not much social life, and that drip is so annoying!" Conqutie whinges.

You turn to look at the puddle behind you, which is continually topped up by a slow drip from the ceiling. It looks to be coming from near the jetty.

"That was the result of one of your predecessors who dived in the lake after me and tried to swim down through the mirror. He was very brave, nice long feet..." she tells you, her eyes drifting away.

"Drowned, of course. And damaged the floor of the lake at the same time, trying to hack through with a grass dagger! Sorry P, your kind just can't cross the mirror. Do you mind if I check my reflection, by the way, can I borrow that big spoon?"

You shake your head apologetically but remember your promise not to reveal Bishroy's whereabouts.

Frustrated, Conqutie storms,

"You've lost it!? Ugh, adventurers these days! Bye x"

She goes to kneel at the silvery puddle and tends to her hair, ignoring you.

You slink away reticently into the tunnels.

If you went this way, turn to page 80.
If you went that way, turn to page 72.

You swim towards the island. Closer now, you can see a heap of black material piled high in the centre of the island. An alarm call sounds as you approach.

A flotilla of enemy craft glides out to meet you. You are not naturally amphibious, and your wet cloak is heavy. An ineffective hull. The armada moves into formation around you, looking for weaknesses, and finding them. You splash hopelessly to scare them off. Two vessels make a feint to your left. You lunge at them with your hands, missing by a wide margin, and a sneak attack strikes you from the right. Ouch, E4 – hit!

You draw any grass weapons you possess, swiping wildly. B9 – miss. The fleet dodges you, and you receive a nasty blow to your left foot. F6 – hit! You flail in rage but are easily outmanoeuvred. A4 – miss. Two bombers strafe overhead, their payload putting your right arm out of action. H2 – hit!

Desperately you make for the shore – if you could only get footing! An opportunistic beak rips away your hat, stabbing at your left hand as you try to hold onto it. G3 – hit!

You are now treading water with only one functioning leg. Floating fish food, you flail a fool's finale. Then, resigning, you lie back in surrender and think of the good times.

A vicious face appears above you as many webbed feet push you under the surface of the Smorgmere. The neck rears back mercilessly, readying for the final stroke. You hear a victorious honking as they celebrate your downfall, then perceive only blackness as the beak hits home.

Hit! Sunk.

Turn to page 12.

You emerge into a wide, hexagonal chamber, almost bumping into Knuckruck as he arrives simultaneously from an adjacent tunnel. He nods to you brusquely, saying,

"Mmph. What are the chances of that? It's like it was meant to be. Well, we've found what we were looking for."

You protest that you didn't know what it is you were looking for in the first place.

"No," he responds, "but you've found it." you sigh as he rattles on, "This is your inevitable destination. The next chapter in your life. Fate."

You argue that you have made conscious decisions on your way here and that this is simply a chance occurrence.

"Mmph. If you think so." the warden asserts curtly.

Disconcerted, you start to assess the cavern. Two tunnels lead into it at 'ground level' from your perspective, or whatever it should be called, given that you are deep underground. The hall is about twice your height, with six black tubes arrayed in the ceiling.

The sound of air being sucked into the overhead pipes is a constant, low thrum, and you can feel a soft turbulence in the room.

"This is the Thoomhub. It's probably at the centre of the mine system, although that's irrelevant, really. In any case, this chamber never collapses. I always come across it at some point during my travels. What does change is where the tunnels take you, the plumbing connections." Knuckruck continues as you look at him vacantly.

"The pipes above are super-fast, frictionless, vacuum transport tubes. They can take you anywhere on the board, immediately. Of course, it's a blind choice." Knuckruck says.

Wow, P, portals! I wonder if there is one that will take you straight to the Baron's castle?

"Shh! I'm trying to deliver an important bit of speech. If you keep interrupting with 'Knuckruck says this, Knuckruck says that', we'll never get anywhere. Anyway, well, portals, yes. But there's a bit more to it than that." Knuckruck says.

"I say anywhere... Really, the tubes can only take you anywhere on the southern upper board. The plumbing only extends as far as we've been able to dig over the years. No excavator has ever been able to extend a seam north under the Smorgaswood – the rock there is like diamond! Too hard. So, no, you can't just thoom your way to the Baron's castle, which, I believe, is roughly north of the Smorgaswood. Sorry.

"If you prefer to walk, the remaining tunnel will route you to other places underground, the lower board. Follow the arrow overleaf if you wish to remain here in the darkness, which I highly recommend." Knuckruck explains, desperate for company.

Come on, P, let's get out of this claustrophobic place. The only advantage of being down here is the lack of Smorgasboards! I suppose they would get broken by rockfalls.

"The thoom technique is very simple; you just stand under a tube of your choice and give a good jump straight off the floor. Before you know, it you'll get sucked off and pop out somewhere – hold onto your hat! One last thing before you go, remember the page number for the Thoomhub! If you arrive at a dead end, you may need to flick straight back here. As I've said, the black barrels are concealed, and if you get stuck somewhere, you may only have one other option to escape..." Knuckruck hints, meaning suicide.

No one wants to have to trek all the way back here from page twelve.

Off you go, P. Your options are displayed pictorially over the page.

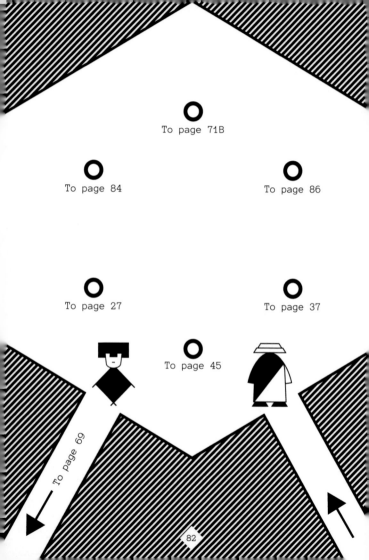

To page 71B

To page 84

To page 86

To page 27

To page 37

To page 45

To page 69

Bibliography:

Edwin A. Abbott, *Flatland: A romance of many dimensions*, originally published by Seeley & Co (1884).

Franz Kafka, *The Trial*, originally published by Verlag Die Schmiede (1925).

Samuel Isaacson, *Escape from Portsrood Forest*, Amazon (2020).

Lewis Carroll, *Alice's Adventures in Wonderland*, originally published by Macmillan (1865).

Mike Russell, *Strungballs*, Strange Books, Amazon (2016).

Acknowledgements:

The Author would like to acknowledge the following for their valuable influences on the development of Smorgasboard:

The game of chess

DROD (Deadly Rooms of Death) by Caravel Games

Ivor Cutler

The Glitch

Cluub Zarathustra

The Dark Room by John Robertson

Thanks to the following for playtesting the book and lending their opinion: Mark Drummond, Lucie Varley, Andy Robertson, Joe Mannion, Alex Green, Alice Mackay, Laura Darby, Maddy Potts and Catherine James.

Thanks to Ruddocks for making Smorgasboard a reality, in particular Verity Stephenson, who has been tremendously helpful with the process of printing and publishing.

THOOM!

You appear inside a narrow cubicle, sitting on a hard, black seat. You appear to have been flushed the wrong way – you are in the WC! Your damp robe leaves an imprint on the toilet seat cover. Seizing opportunity, you lift your cloak and use the facilities. On the inside of the door in front of you is a poster – it's a mini Smorgasboard.

Board #13
Bing bong!

Let them eat urinal cake!

Just taking the P!
Yours, Bongo

You put your head in your hands. Has Bongo lost his mind? On the floor of the WC, you notice a spare roll of toilet paper. You tidy yourself up and **add it** to your inventory, just in case. Looking up, you realise that the poster has changed! How did that happen? It no longer bears the symbol of Smorg but is a hastily written note saying,

Conkers vs Honkers!
You're doing ever so well dear, come and see me in my office and I will answer your questions.

The Decision Tree, Copse 101, Smorgaswood.
Your Servant.

You try the door but are unable to open it, even though the latch is unfastened. You push against the door and can peer through the crack. You glimpse some scrubby trees nearby and, behind them, some pointy hills on either side of a dry valley – it's the gorge from page sixteen, of course. You can't get out; the door is held shut by tape that has been wrapped tightly around the cubicle.

You can just about make out the words on the tape:

CRIME SCENE - DO NOT ENTER

Your options are limited. You are stuck inside a bog.
I suggest you return to the Thoomhub; do you remember the
page number? I'll help you out this time. It's on page 82.

Exhibit G

N

THOOM!

You appear in the middle of a blinding, white desert.
The board lies horizontal all around you; it looks like you
must be in the tundra. Almost entirely featureless, your
only guide is the page numbers and the floating compass in
the sky.

Hopelessly lost, you turn eastwards, as is tradition.

Dismayed and disoriented, you begin to lose track of time. How can you possibly hope to reach the Baron's castle, P?

Eventually, a distant post comes into view, stark against the pale flatness. You detect an acrid smell, like burnt paper, and realise that the post has been blackened by fire.

An incident has occurred here.

This used to be a Smorgasboard. Glancing around, you spot the torched notice nearby, discarded on the floor like a disposable barbecue. Who would sabotage Bongo's boards? The edges are charred. You can just make out the text.

Board #14
Bing bong!

All terrorists will be sought out and destroyed.

Yours, Bongo

Is that a joke? There's no pun.
Maybe it's one of those poems that doesn't rhyme.

As you finish studying the board, you sense that you are no longer alone. You can't see anyone else, as such, but feel that eyes are observing you. You scratch your head and sniff the air; something smells fishy. It could just be you after your dip in the lake?

You continue in the same direction, and your peripheral vision gradually becomes aware of dark dots on the horizon to your rear. Others! When you spin (clockwise), the others seem to duck down, and you cannot pinpoint them.

This continues for some time, adding to your paranoia. Finally, what looks like some ruins appear ahead – sanctuary? You increase your speed across the plain, but the dots seem to outpace you.

The others work their way to your front until they nearly encompass you. Clearly hostile, they begin to jeer at you, baying for blood. You have no idea where you are, who these pursuers are or what they want... FLEE to the ruins!

To 92A

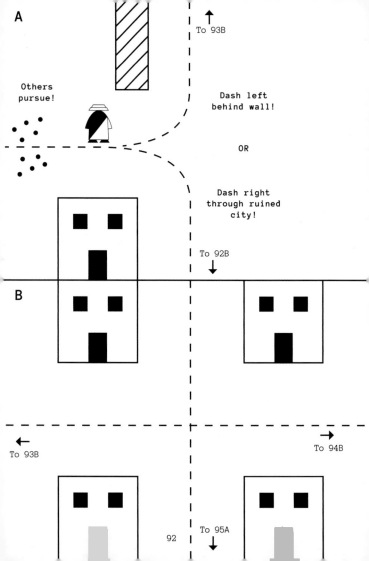

A

Others
pursue!

To 93B

Dash left
behind wall!

OR

Dash right
through ruined
city!

To 92B

B

To 93B

To 94B

92

To 95A

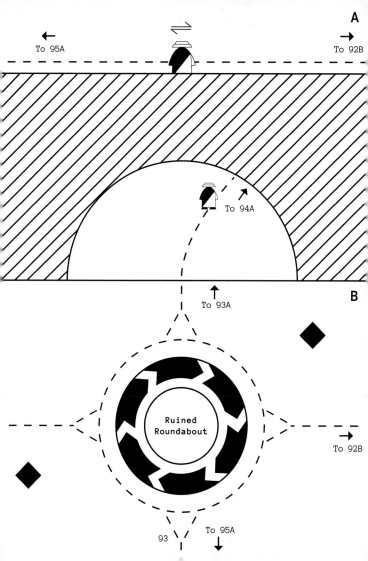

To 95A

To 92B

A

To 94A

B

To 93A

Ruined
Roundabout

To 92B

To 95A

93

A

The others corner you in an alley, they have you surrounded.
A big one pops up and bonks you on the head.

It's a
dead end!

BONK!

Turn to
page 96.

B

To 93A

To 92B

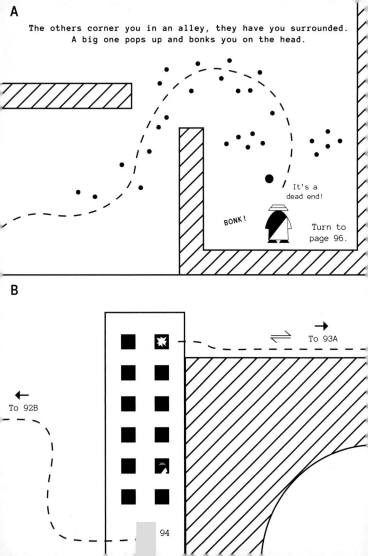

94

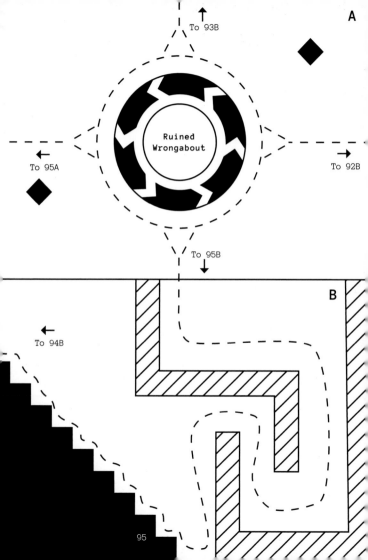

To 93B

Ruined
Wrongabout

To 95A

To 92B

To 95B

To 94B

You awake, groggy, on the floor of a dank cell. You hear a muffled voice, "We've got it!" and then another in a higher pitch, "Yes, yes, now quick, take it to the boss!"

A cage slams and the sound of steps recedes into the distance, and then the voices are gone. Rising slowly, you feel your cloak is askew and that you have been rummaged around. Clearly, you have been captured and... beaten? You can't remember anything since that bonk to the head. You pat yourself down to find that all your weapons have been taken. ~~Cross out any grass items~~ from your inventory. Your hat lies crumpled on the floor; you sweep it up, straighten it out and replace it with a practised motion.

"Nice hat, shame about the colour." a low voice drawls. You are not alone. You stumble to the edge of the cell, seeing double, and grip onto the cage. It is constructed from the stiff reed canes that you have seen around the lake. Through the bars, you see – is it an optical illusion? Negative, it's real, but the colour is all opposite. A guard stands watch over you from underneath a nice, black hat.

That bonk on the head has had an unusual effect. If you close one eye, the double vision resolves, but this is not just ordinary double vision: You find that if you close your left eye, you see the world through the eyes of the prison guard, Q. If you close the right eye, you remain behind bars as the prisoner, P.

It's Q, not you.

To temporarily switch character to Q, turn to page 99.

To remain true to yourself as P, turn to page 98.

You examine the guard on the other side of the bars. His shoulders slumped, he looks tired. You wonder if he has the key.

"Where am I? Who is holding me prisoner here?" you demand to know. You demand to know!? Oh, so you can speak now, can you, P? Typical. I've been talking at you for 98 pages, with you plodding along in silence the whole way, and now after a bonk on the head, you start talking!

"The Ωthers have taken you captive." Q drawls in reply. "Who are the others? Am I in the Baron's castle? Is Bongo the bard held here too?" you query. What's this, dialogue!? I bet you're going to be a chatterbox until the end now, aren't you? You shrug. Although his mouth is hidden, you detect a smirk in Q's reply,

"Others are people that aren't you. The Ωthers are the resistance. You are certainly not in the Baron's castle. The clown is not here. I can say no more. Boss's orders."

"Who is your boss? Who do you work for?" you quiz.
"I work for the guard commander."
"Who does he work for?"
"Umm, shrug. Another boss, I suppose. That's how it works."
Is this foot soldier an idiot?

"I want to speak to the guard commander immediately. Can you fetch him?"
"Certainly, but I need permission to do that."
"How do you get permission?"
"From the guard commander."
"Bring him here then!"
"Not without permission."

You shout in frustration, hoping to attract attention, "HELP!!"
"Certainly. If you find yourself at the end of your tether, prove yourself. One cannot argue with deductive inferences." Q drawls cryptically.

You blink, and the double vision resolves. Turn to page 112.

You examine the creature behind bars. A pathetic sight. This one looks exhausted. All the better for your purposes; easy to manipulate. You wonder if he is the key.

"Where am I? Who is holding me prisoner here?" P demands to know.

"The Ωthers have taken you captive," you reply with disdain.

Hmm, dialogue from the detainee. You'll have to control that wagging tongue. But not here, later, later.

"Who are the others? Am I in the Baron's castle? Is Bongo the bard held here too?" your captive asks, confused. It appears he is still intent on a rescue attempt. How naïve. His own worst enemy.

"Others are people that aren't you. The Ωthers are the resistance. You are certainly not in the Baron's castle. The clown is not here. I can say no more. Boss's orders." you answer, followed by an amusing exchange in which you feign ignorance.

The prisoner shouts for help in frustration, hoping to attract attention.

Not much time left to lay your plan, you need to get him out of here, but only the guard commander can open the cage. You know how the boss is likely to adjudicate but cannot risk intervening openly here.

Hoping P will catch on, you hint, "Certainly. If you find yourself at the end of your tether, prove yourself. One cannot argue with deductive inferences."

Hearing others approach, you stand to attention, guarding diligently.

You blink, and both eyes open to find that the double vision has resolved, and you are P once more.

Turn to page 112.

Feathers settle after the battle, but there is no time to celebrate. You travel with Shah Franz and his captains northeast from the lake up the grassy lane. The majority of Ωthers remain behind to begin shipping rhombi back from the island to Pagefortytown. Shah Franz informs you they intend to re-open the power plant. You demand more detail about his battle plan en route. He tells you there are limited seats in the APC: He prefers to move fast rather than get bogged down with the logistics of moving his entire force and that this type of operation is better suited to a smaller, elite team. You look around at him, Knuckruck, Conqutie, Lance and yourself and are not much reassured by this so-called elitism. You are led on a march through the meadows until the party arrives at a large trampoline.

"Well, no time to waste. Proceed, Guard Commander."
Shah Franz instructs.

Sir Poignée de L'ansa begins chopping at the elasticated floor, which peels back, exposing a ramp leading underground. You descend into a Smorgasgarage to discover the Armoured Personnel Carrier.

YOUR AD HERE

"It's a bus." you state to Shah Franz, unimpressed.

"A Rhombus!" he beams back, "Ah Q, there you are. What have you been up to? Have you prepared the vehicle?" as Q appears from underneath the chassis with a box of tools and a soiled rag. You detect a peculiar eau de toilette.

"Yes, boss, everything's fixed."
Q gives assent. Your nose twitches as he sweeps by.

"Marvellous. We head north. All aboard!" Shah Franz calls.

With Q at the wheel, the Rhombus trundles north to the border of the Smorgaswood, past the barrel and into the shade of the forest. You manage about a dozen smorgmetres before the first diamond shard slams into the roof, leaving a dent. The drumming of glass overhead sets music to your fears, and you grip your seat as the bus ploughs on through the deadly autumn.

The bus takes a tortuous route through the dark forest, and you worry that Q will become lost. Fortunately, the word count demands a pacy narrative, and before you know it, the bus pulls over. Its engine sighs as the driver announces that you have arrived at a palindromic prime.

"Copse 101!"

You make to exit the bus, but your companions do not share your enthusiasm. You find it impossible to make eye contact with any of the Ωthers, and Sir Poignée de L'ansa sits there whistling avoidantly. You alight the bus alone, keeping an eye on the leaves above.

Three trees loom. The central tree looks like the other diamond-leaved species growing throughout the Smorgaswood, but is much taller, as if this great plant has spread seedlings across the board. You crane your neck upwards and spot a high platform amongst the web of branches. The leaves twinkle, and you experience a mild sensation of glitter blowing in your face, although the air is quite still. This is the fabled Decision Tree, and the other two are immediately familiar to you: On the east of the copse is a commanding oak tree with ridged, brown bark and a dome of deep green leaves. The colour is stark against the monochrome of the board. To the west stands an equally impressive specimen of horse chestnut in all its pomp; large, green, palmate leaves cover a scaly trunk. These incongruous trees are known to you from your own world – how can they be here?

Fallen glass leaves splinter underfoot as you cross the ground to the base of the Decision Tree. 'Crunch, crunch, crunch', onomatopoeia again, you tread carefully.

Around the girth of the mighty trunk is carved a spiral staircase. You stop, peering into the heights, but oddly the sound of your footsteps continues. Listening closely, you realise it is no longer a crunch but a munch. The noise fades like an echo. You begin the ascent. Needing to keep a close eye on the narrow steps does not allow for much scrutiny of your surroundings, but you catch glimpses of movement around you as you climb. What sort of creature would live here? Squirrels? Shy edges and timid shadows disappear behind leaves and branches, accompanied by the sound of gnawing. As you ascend, the glimpses increase, and the chorus rises as if a throng of chomping creatures is following you up the tree.

Puffing, you arrive beneath the high platform. A dangling ladder offers entry through a trapdoor in the floor. You pull yourself up and collapse on the decking, now surrounded by the chewing denizens of the Decision Tree. They are difficult to describe, but you observe them clearly now, feeling that they have allowed you into their secret habitat.

"Providence, providence!"

A voice pierces the munching, strikingly familiar.

"Oh, hello dear, welcome to the Decision Tree."

The voice croaks as you look around. Where have you heard it before? Of course, the Providore!

A pair of feet lands in front of you, the owner having leapt from a branch overhead. They are nice feet, lithe and hefty. You attempt to disguise your own clods with your cloak as you stand to greet an unspecified sprite. You are momentarily baffled as she appears both beautiful and terrifying, but somehow you can't decide which.

Nevertheless, you are simultaneously awestruck by beauty and stricken with terror. For some reason, you find yourself raising your robe as you perform a deep curtsy.

"Um, hello. My name is..."

"P. Yes, I know, dear." the sprite smiles kindly or unkindly.

"I've been watching you very closely since page six. It was I who brought you the visions, at Bongo's request, as I'm sure you have realised. You needn't kneel - I am your servant. I have done my best to speed your journey here."

"Mm. Thank you for the flumps. Have you been hiding in the cracks between pages as well? I thought the Ωthers didn't trust you? Or is it that you have - magic?" you query sheepishly.

"Aha, no, nothing so crude." the sprite explains, "I have never left this treehouse. The answer you seek lies all around you. These are my trusted guardians, messengers, devotees."

The nondescript nymph gestures tenderly or grandly to the short, squat creatures arrayed around you on the deck. They briefly cease chewing to nod towards you in acknowledgement.

"These are the source of all my power. A well-kept secret, the Unknown Gnomes!" the unspecified sprite announces.

The gnomes halt their meal to perform a ceremonial near-dance for their idol. They shuffle around her as if she were a maypole before settling back into position. They pull pieces of white material out from their pockets and, in unison, stuff it into their mouths with a ravenous,

"Gnome gnom nom nom..."

Curious things, I would describe them in more detail, but the words elude me. As I've said, they are short, squat creatures, but more than that, well... I can tell you that they don't have hats. Perplexed, you turn back to the sprite,

"Who? What are they? What do you mean unknown, what are they eating, and why are they so vague?"

"I told you, P, they are the Unknown Gnomes! You've come across them before, but you didn't read about them. It was the gnomes that put Bongo's letter in your hand and accidentally dropped the flumps you required, though, of course, you wouldn't have seen that in the text. Under my instruction, they created your visions, by which I mean they pinned you down and blew glitter in your face before amending the transcript." the sprite explains.

"They are responsible for many things that otherwise might seem like co-incidences. Have you ever noticed that the signage changes around here? Who do you think amends the Smorgasboards?

"Gnomes, my dear.

"They are my anonymous footmen, invisible agents." she concludes.

"But how do they remain unseen? And why can I read about them now?" you ask.

"They eat the paper, of course; they don't like the taste, but it keeps anyone from writing anything about them! Their actions simply go undocumented. As to why you can see them now, well, you've arrived here at their home and discovered their existence – they have become Known Gnomes! To you, at least. They're a shy bunch, though, I doubt they would allow any detailed description of them to be published." the sprite informs you.

Wondering if you have bitten off more than you can chew by entering the Smorgasboard, you consider the elusive nature of the gnomes. Pressing the sprite, you enquire further,

"What about Unknown Ungnomes – do they exist too?"

"I'm not aware of any," she responds, "but I wouldn't be even if they did."

"So, are you saying that, feasibly, there are even more unseen beings that act outside of our awareness; pursuing their own opaque agendas?" you extrapolate, wondering if you really are the author of your own destiny.

"Well, I suppose it's possible." she answers cynically or impressed by your insight.

Desperate to escape this place, your intellectual prowess immediately diminishes as you stroll around the platform and begin yelling to the ether,

"HELP!! HELP!! I SPEAK TO THE UNKNOWN UNGNOMES! PLEASE GET ME OUT OF HERE!!"

You wait on the edge of the treehouse, looking out across the canopy. You hope to be beamed up by hyperintelligent beings, but the diamond leaves just blink back at you, and the chewing sound predominates once more.

I've wanted to tell you about the gnomes all this time, P, but they just devour literature. It's a useful trick if you can stomach it. Give it a go – I've said something mean about you at the edge of the treehouse over there.

Bite the edge off the page to remove that slander!

For legal purposes, don't swallow anything. Smorgasboard will not be held responsible for your bizarre habits.

BITE HERE:

P struggles to
comprehend metaphor and
will likely be trapped in
Smorgasboard forever!

The unspecified sprite pats you on the back gently or firmly and invites you to sit down.

"I'm sensing that you are a little tense. How can I help?"

You cannot sit but instead pace around the decking. Your mind races over all you have learnt, and your thoughts tumble out,

"Is Smorgasboard anything more than this – a decision tree? Am I really in a forest or just trapped in an algorithm?"

The unspecified sprite stands by pensively or otherwise. Frustrated by her vague silence, you continue,

"Is it just input/output – a simple machine? Or can Smorgasboard learn? Is it sentient?"

The sprite responds calmly or derisively,

"It has already learnt many things about you. Your choices have revealed your character. Your appreciation of themes and motifs has been logged. It holds your biometric data, and it has embedded itself into your memory circuits. When you opened this book, you entered the Smorgasboard. Now it has entered you. You may close the book, but you cannot delete it. You have given it sentience. It has been subsumed into your life story, and it has subsumed you into its narrative, and vice versa."

With your head in your hands, you sit on the floor and try to breathe. You feel there are still so many unanswered questions. You try to focus on the information you require. Exploding again, you demand of this so-called oracle:

"What do you know about Bongo? Do you really think he can help me escape? Are the Smorgasboards relevant or just part of the trap? How do I get to the castle and thwart the Baron? Why does he have guard geese, and where did they come from? How can I defeat them? What items will I need to carry? What was the providore all about? Why haven't you helped the Ωthers defend their homeland? Can I trust you? Where are we – where did those other trees come from, and why am I here?!" you breakdown, weeping.

The unspecified sprite sighs, "Oh dear, lots of questions. This is slightly unorthodox, but I think it may be best at this point if I provide you with a glossary."

Glossary

Baron Smorg:
An evil overlord, he fills the classic 'bad guy' trope. He has trapped you in the Smorgasboard and is causing chaos. An old flame. It is not clear how you can thwart him.

Bongo:
The Baron's court jester. He is imprisoned in the castle and has asked for your help. He is responsible for the Smorgasboards, which display his jokes throughout the land. His humour is becoming more obscure, and there are serious concerns for his mental health. I took pity on him and agreed to alert you of his plight. Rescue him, if you can.

Castle:
A difficult-to-reach final destination, the fortress of the Baron. It lies to the north of the forest.

Items:
Objects carried in your inventory. Some are more useful than others. Cordage is always useful.

Geese:
Bullies who push ducks off donated bread. Intrinsically funny, like cheese, trombones, or hats. Hired thugs, an invasive species imported from your world and employed by the Baron as a 'foreign legion' of brutal soldiers. They can be scared by loud noises but will fight when cornered. They

are impervious to most attacks but are vulnerable to rhyme. Over the page is a cut-out origami model of the enemy for you to study. Cut carefully along the lines and fold down the plane of symmetry to construct a free-standing goose.

Ωthers:
Native insurgents. A resistance movement revolting against the Baron's occupation, the two sides are engaged in information warfare. Led by Shah Franz, they have adopted you into their ranks. They don't trust me, although I am friendly towards them. Unfortunately, I cannot risk supporting them more openly, having my own realm to consider should you fail.

Providence:
1. Divine guidance and care, destiny.

2. The quality or state of being provident, the act of providing, e.g. supplies of food.

Providore:
The providore is one of my outposts in the upper board. Its primary purpose is to supply adventurers with items to assist them through the Baron's maze. In addition, I am hoarding flumps to feed my gnomes in an underground larder.

Smorgasbo(a)rd:
1. An assortment, an assemblage, a variety.

2. A buffet of hot and cold dishes, commonly meats. Presented on a table or platter.

3. An interactive fiction, ISBN 978-0-904327-35-9.

4. A signpost displaying 'Smorgas' – the literary works of Bongo the bard.

5. A monochrome country with a diverse, rhomboid landscape. Exists on paper and in the imagination of the reader. Inhabited by Smorgasians.

6. A comedy algorithm simulating artificial stupidity.

Trees:
Tall plants bearing leaves. The Decision Tree is the parent which has spread its deadly diamond-leaved progeny to form the Smorgaswood. Copse 101 contains two other particular specimens which have been imported from your world by a traveller: an oak and a horse chestnut.

Trust:
Confidence placed in an individual or group. Only you can decide who to trust. Unfortunately, people do not always turn out to be who you thought they were.

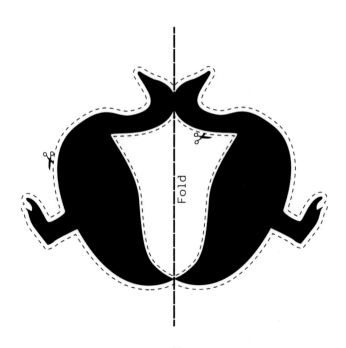

Fold

You feel that the glossary has answered some of your questions but raised others, and you are alert for disinformation. You look down at your clods in thought and suddenly realise that the platform itself is an oversized Smorgasboard, displaying more of Bongo's poetry. It seems the Baron's influence may extend as far as this woody enclave.

Board #15
Bing bong!

Fruit and nut held high
Threaded string of syllables
A treehouse haiku

We need to talk – it's not you, it's me.
Your Bongo

"I hope that the glossary was helpful," the unspecified sprite smiles or smirks, "now I would like to offer you a gift before you depart our Leafy Independent Zone."

She opens her hands to reveal an acorn and a conker.

The sprite continues graciously or reluctantly,

"These are the first fruits of the two green trees you see here. I have a great affinity to trees and have cultivated those two for a very long time since they were but fruits themselves. They were brought to me by an adventurer, not unlike yourself, who had journeyed far, down many roads, even into other worlds. I adopted them and raised them as saplings beside the Decision Tree, and it gives me joy to see them become parents themselves. Though it pains me to part, I want you to take one of them. I see many things from this high platform, and it is clear to me that you will need everything I can give you."

You eye the nuts in her palms and raise an eyebrow,

"Everything? Can't I have them both, then?"

The treehouse suddenly goes silent, the munching sound ceases, and the Known Gnomes stare at you fixedly. A few start inching around to the blind spot at your rear. The sprite looks disappointed or amused.

"It will be one, and only one, my dear. Acorn or conker?" she says lightly or with gravity.

Take either Acorn OR Conker to add to your inventory.

"Farewell, dear. May it serve you well."

The unspecified sprite signals to her followers, and you blink as you feel a glittery sensation blowing in your face. When you open your eyes, you are back at the base of the tree, with no memory of the descent. You suspect gnomes.

Return to the bus, which waits for you on page 126.

To your surprise, Sir Poignée de L'ansa strides into the
room, and Q snaps to attention. Of course, he is the guard
commander! You sigh relief to see a friendly face, or
shield. He looks at you apologetically through the bars,
then gestures to others waiting behind him. Before you know
it, you are manhandled out of the cell, your hat pulled down
around your eyes. You are bundled down narrow passages and
then into a wide chamber which resounds with chatter. A
crowd jeers as you are brought in roughly and bound to a
chair.

Your hat is loosened, and you are able to look around.
You are in the centre of a large, square courtroom. Raked
benches rise steeply to either side and behind you, occupied
to the rafters by a murmuring mob. The fourth 'wall' in
front of you is a set of heavy curtains, the whole height
of the room. In front of them, a plinth supports a throne
which engulfs a small individual who you assume to be
overseeing proceedings. The judge sits still, barely moving
at all, analysing you with deadly focus.

You are surprised to see Conqutie close by on the front bench; she wears a commanding black gown. Surely she can get you out of this tight spot. You also see Knuckruck in the crowd who gives you a terse nod, and Lance stands guard at the door to your rear. He smiles weakly. Others fill the dimly lit pews, their dark shapes whisper accusations and occasionally point at you. They immediately drop silent as the magistrate begins speaking in an archaic legal dialect,

"The defendant now being present, I will hear the case of Ωthers v P pursuant to our statutory proceedings insofar as is necessary to appreciate the actions a priori as claimed by the plaintiff hereunto. The charges?"

To your astonishment, Conqutie stands to address the court and lays out the indictment made against you – she is the prosecuting barrister!

"Thank you, Shah Franz," she says to the judge, then turns to you accusingly.

"1. Possession of a bladed article in a public place," she starts coolly. She points at a desk behind her that displays your grass weaponry, recently confiscated. Others in the stalls examine the table with disapproving tones.

"Do you deny it?" Shah Franz quizzes you sharply.
"No, but..." you begin to say before murmurs break out in the court. Shah Franz calls the assembly to order, and Conqutie continues,

"2. Wilful damage to personal property."

"3. Unauthorised trespass to land."

Whispers reach you from the benches, "Just wouldn't stop kicking the barrel."
Conqutie points to your footprints on the evidence table, labelled Exhibit E and Exhibit F.

"Are these your feet?" Shah Franz demands.
"Yes, but..." you begin, but are drowned out by the crowd,

"Those are his feet! Brazen! Shameless! Clods!"

"4. Operating an unregistered vessel on an inland waterway without a license." Conqutie presses on.

"What, the raft?! You lot fired arrows at me!" you retort. Intimidating jeers from the Ωthers in the crowd silence you.

"5. Theft." the prosecution states simply, pointing at Exhibit A and B, which display your fingerprints.

"Are these your aforementioned fingerprints?" Shah Franz asks.

"Well, I don't know, how did you get those?" you reply.

Conqutie seizes on this,
"He doesn't even know what his hands have been doing!" she announces, to shocked outbursts from the room. You stare, open-mouthed, at the barrister whom you thought an ally.

"6. Gawping." she indicts, to approval from the Ωthers.

"Gawping? Is that a crime?" you demand of the judge.
"It's a verb. And we didn't ask for a demonstration." Shah Franz replies, "The final charge?"

"7. Indecent exposure in front of a minor." Conqutie asserts, to a general hush. Two small others shuffle from a bench to take to the stand near Shah Franz. Conqutie addresses them,

"It is very brave of you to bear witness today. If you could please describe the event in question."

The little one sniffs, then delivers a sob story which you can barely believe,

"Well, your honour, me and the other one were out playing like normal. I know we shouldn't have been away from home, but we were so bored with hiding. So we snook out to page sixteen, and we were just minding our own business playing

114

tig around the trees when... that person there, comes along and..."

"Take your time, dear," soothes Conqutie, "what did the defendant do?"

The little one tries to go on but is weeping too much. The other one continues,

"Right in front of us, they flashed their bits from under their cloak." she says, to audible gasps from the courtroom.

"On page sixteen, you say?" the prosecution probes.
"I swear on my life. Turn back to see it if you need – it's all there!"

In ascendancy, Conqutie presses home,

"Ladies and Gentlemen, I am sure I needn't lecture you on the layout of Smorgasboard. You will all be aware of the WC on page seventeen – clearly labelled for all travellers, mere smorgmetres away from the incident in question! There can be no doubt this heinous crime was done with intent."

Outrage spreads through the crowd. Shah Franz brings the court to order once more,

"Bring forth the final piece of evidence."

"Certainly, your honour, allow me to present a print taken in custody earlier today. Ladies and Gentlemen, the offending item!" Conqutie declares triumphantly.

Two sturdy others carry in a white sheet, large enough to be seen from the back row. It is labelled 'Exhibit H' and displays a black and white print of your undercarriage.

"Do you recognise this, children? Does it match what you witnessed during the incident on page sixteen?"

"That's them!" the little one screams.
"Disgusting!" the other one howls.

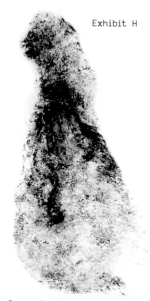

Exhibit H

At least two members of the jury are sick, and another swoons. Her examination complete, Conqutie returns to the bench, self-satisfied. Your head hangs. I wonder if that is actually the author's undercarriage? Surely not.

Perhaps he mocked it up with some chicken skin and a bit of fluff from under the rug. If you wish to imprint your own more accurate or gender-specific undercarriage, the inside rear cover is blank for this purpose.

Shah Franz sighs and leans over, looking at you. "Allow me to summarise the case for the court. Manifestly, we have been collecting data about you for some time. Prints, biometrics, height, width, depth...

Our spies have been hiding in plain sight, in the open, amongst punctuation. We have been keeping a close eye on you, P. The allegations have been put forward. I consider the last charge so serious that I deemed it fit and proper for this trial to be heard before a full plenary of our organisation. The evidence is apparent; our children had strayed from the page margin to play in the copse when they witnessed YOU exhibiting yourself in all your perverse glory."

The judge concludes, "You have heard the charges. How do you plead?"

To plead guilty, continue reading.
To plead not guilty, turn to page 117.

"The jury has delivered a guilty verdict. I will now deliberate upon a sentence." Shah Franz proclaims.

"What!" you interrupt, "When did they? They've only just heard the evidence! They've had no chance to retire to consider any verdict! This trial is a farce!" the room hushes. Shah Franz explains to you laconically,

"That is contempt of court. This may surprise you, P, but time is not necessarily linear within literature. And this, after all, is an experimental, postmodernist meta-fiction."

"Oh, right." you answer, thinking that the whole thing sounds rather pretentious, "What happens now, then?"

"I was about to sentence you before I was rudely adjourned. So that will happen next, after this pointless diversion."

"Wait!" you cry with epiphany, causing the judge to sigh, "What if I just keep speaking? If I keep speaking until the end of the book, I won't give you a chance to sentence me! Ha! As long as I don't stop talking you are powerless to do anything! Blah blah blah. Dum du dumm. Erm, so what shall I talk about now, can't stop, not even for a second. Umm, the weather, people always talk about that, don't they? There hasn't been much mention of weather since I entered the Smorgasboard, though, a bit of wind, that's about it. Err, not sure, what else..." you pause feebly.

Shah Franz cracks a grim smile.
"I admire your audacity, P, but you are not in control here. You have gotten this far, page 117 indeed, but no further. I sentence you to death forthwith." Shah Franz states, stunning you into disbelief.

Clamours from the crowd ring out, "Burn him!" calls one. "Erase, cancel, delete!" cries another. "Tear him in half!" yells a third.

Shah Franz shakes his head a notch,
"We are not cruel. The execution will be swift. Bring forth the gallows."

C H _ _ C K M A T _

Hoisted up, the Ωthers yell out letters as you are slowly strangled. It does feel cruel to you, although you suppose that that is subjective. Choked by the noose, you desperately try to persuade Shah Franz:

"Wait! If you kill me, I will simply go back to page twelve! It might take a while, but I'll just come back here all over again! And I'll have to go via page sixteen, returning to the scene of the crime; I'll be forced to re-offend! Think of the children!"

The crowd pauses, the final letter on their lips. You scrabble at the rope in desperation. All look to Shah Franz. He deliberates in silence, fingers poised together.

"The logic is undeniable," he concludes, "release the prisoner."

Cheers of joy ring out from the volatile crowd. The noose is removed from your neck, and you are welcomed by the jostling mob. Many Ωthers pat you on the back. Shah Franz meets your gaze, and for the first time you sense some warmth emanate from him.

"Well, P, you have saved yourself. But the guilty verdict still stands; instead, I deem that you will assist us. I sentence you to community service. You will join our forces and help us rid this land of the invaders. Your knowledge of the enemy may prove useful versus the same."

"We will now convene a Council of War." Shah Franz announces to the court.

A Council of War

At time of reading
Location: Shah Franz' chambers

MINUTES

Present: Chair – Shah Franz (SF), Guard Commander – Sir
Poignée de L'ansa (SPDL), Attorney General – Conqutie (C),
Chief Mining Controller – Knuckruck (K), You – P (P), Other
Ωthers – Others (Ω), Scribe – Narrator.

Apologies: Prison Guard – Q (Q)

Absent: Chief Mourner – Bishroy (B).

Agenda:
1. Preliminaries: Minutes and matters arising
2. Situation and Ground
3. Our forces
4. Enemy forces
5. Actions agreed
6. Any other business

1. The meeting was called to order by the chair. The
standing orders were read and understood. Minutes of the
previous meeting were approved with universal gloom. A
toast was raised to absent friends lost at the battle
of Pagefortytown. SPDL confirmed that an APC had been
constructed per the last meeting.

2. SF explained that although the board may seem
uninhabited now, it would usually be a thriving centre of
life and industry. Unfortunately, due to Baron Smorg's
policies, most of the Smorgasians have been made redundant,
or worse. The mines were closed, and the residents forced
underground. The Ωthers now represent the only remaining
resistance to his rule.

P queried what the mining industry was extracting in the
first place. K stated that rhombi were the major natural
resource.

Ω shouted, "rhombuses!" before being silenced by the chair. K clarified that the slag heaps lying all over the place were not mere decoration but that the rhombi form the very fabric of the board itself. P stated they just looked like black squares in the background, to general discontent.

P queried how rhombi form in the first place. K explained that straight lines are compressed under immense pressure over a long period of time until they form a quadrilateral whose four sides all have the same length. P asked where the straight lines came from originally.

SF highlighted that, in the beginning, Smorgasboard was just blank paper. Aeons ago, lines were added to the paper, and it was folded to form a book. The author made notes on the lines to construct the ideas which became the present text. Many notebooks were used in this dark past, and many lines discarded.

P (verbatim): And Smorgasboard – this is what remains? The best the author could come up with?

SF: So it would seem. Over time thousands of lines melted away into the ground, geological strata crushed on top of each other, forming the bedrock of this land and the underground seams of rhombi that we now quarry.

P asked the council if rhombi were a fossil fuel like coal and whether they would run out. K acknowledged that the black diamonds can be burnt for fuel but that no fossils are harmed in the process. K stated that rhombi appear to be renewable and that new seams were always forming. Consensus was that in the other world, the goose world, lines are still being printed, and ideas are still being written down, although the fate of the author is unknown.

SF (verbatim): Reports of his death may be a ruse of the Baron's. Amongst our most arcane scholars, there are even rumours of a sequel, but we do not speak of such things.

SPDL concluded the ground brief, stating that the weather forecast was good, with a mild northerly breeze.

3. SF explained that he had ordered the Ωthers to follow then capture P as a potential threat. There was a concern that P, being from the goose world, was another of the Baron's mercenaries. The entry bridge had been blown up by the resistance to prevent further reinforcements.

SF stated that the Smorgasians had been forcibly evicted from their homes in Pagefortytown and that the Baron had been deceived into believing they had literally gone underground into the tunnels.

SF (verbatim): The Baron didn't build this place, you know! He might profess that he owns it all, but this is contrivance. We have our own secrets.
P: Where have you been hiding then?
SF: In the cracks between pages, of course! We can move through the book as we will, notwithstanding the fact that straying out in plain sight risks being apprehended.

SF highlighted that the Ωthers had not been idle whilst holed out. It was revealed that our forces have been developing a way of moving across the pages of the board protected from attack; based on a vehicle from the goose world, made with local materials - an APC!

P: What's an APC?
SPDL: It's an acronym.
P: Yes, but what does it stand for?
SPDL: Armoured Personnel Carrier.

P agreed to join the Ωthers as an auxiliary.

4. C put forward the motion that the Baron's guard geese are imported mercenaries who have stolen Smorgasboard from its native inhabitants and should be considered alien invaders. The motion was seconded by SPDL, carried.

C relayed the most up-to-date intelligence re the enemy; that they have taken the island on the lake as their stronghold and have been observed stockpiling rhombi there. C reported that the rhombi had been seized from the homes of residents who had been left in fuel poverty.

The Baron appears to want to control the flow of rhombi for his own opaque purposes. C also reported that regular foot patrols had been observed across the board, with additional flying sorties conducting aerial surveillance. It was, however, considered unlikely that the Baron had discovered the location of the Ωthers at this time.

SPDL demanded of P knowledge re how to kill a goose, stating that all the traditional ways had been tried, including silver bullets, garlic, and sunlight – all ineffective. P explained they are not mythical creatures, just geese.

SPDL (verbatim): They're mythical to us!
Ω: They hiss! They honk!
SPDL: They can break a man's arm, you know.
Ω: The feet! The beaks!
P: Is that not a swan?
SPDL: A what?
P: Doesn't matter.

Both parties agreed to defer the issue.

SPDL: Every time we come up against these geese, we are defeated. Perhaps you have experienced this yourself? We are outnumbered and outgunned.

Ω: Outgoosed!

P raised smorgrass as a readily available and very lethal-looking weapon. SPDL reassured the foreigner that all manner of grass weaponry had already been tried. A few feathers had been dislodged, but the geese were too large, too fast, and too angry to defeat via these means. Nevertheless, P requested the return of his grass dagger for personal protection. SF approved the motion, and it was **added once more** to the inventory.

P suggested trying a very loud bang, as noise scares off most birds. SPDL outlined problems with the procurement of high explosives, which are kept under lock and key in the castle armoury.

P queried whether the council had knowledge of a sprite who was known to do Bongo's bidding. SF stated that they were aware of a powerful enchantress or oracle who dwells at Copse 101 in the Smorgaswood but that it had been difficult to gain accurate intelligence reports on this individual. For security purposes, therefore, she is to be considered an enemy until proven otherwise.

There was broad disillusionment with Bongo's boards which were considered a distraction. SF stated that it is his policy to burn all the boards they find, but unfortunately, unseen actors keep re-erecting them.

P volunteered to lead an assault on the island but, in return, requested assistance in getting to the castle. It was discussed that the APC would be necessary to cross the Smorgaswood to avoid being dashed to bits by loose leaves. There was reluctant agreement.

5. A mission was put forward by SF:
To destroy the geese and recapture the island, clearing enemy in the southern board to set the conditions for further advance north via Smorgaswood to Castle in order to apprehend Baron Smorg and effect regime change.

The motion was carried unanimously.

6. C raised whether it would be possible to find a more competent reader. The council unanimously agreed with the motion but, given the urgency of the circumstances, conceded the current reader would have to suffice.

The council of war was brought to a close.

After the meeting, some burly Ωthers draw back the hefty curtains behind Shah Franz, and you see that you have been on stage the whole time. As the militia files out through the dilapidated double doors onto the street, you realise that you were behind the curtain of the theatre in Pagefortytown! This is ideal for your cunning plan, and you suggest to Shah Franz a short diversion to pick up more equipment en route to battle.

THE BATTLE OF GOOSE ISLAND

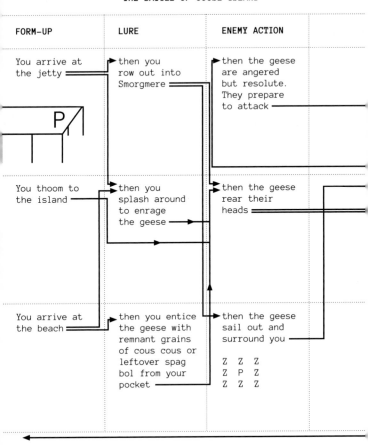

FORM-UP	LURE	ENEMY ACTION
You arrive at the jetty	then you row out into Smorgmere	then the geese are angered but resolute. They prepare to attack
You thoom to the island	then you splash around to enrage the geese	then the geese rear their heads
You arrive at the beach	then you entice the geese with remnant grains of cous cous or leftover spag bol from your pocket	then the geese sail out and surround you

```
Z   Z   Z
Z   P   Z
Z   Z   Z
```

INSTRUCTIONS: Choose a starting point, then read left to right to form a sentence. Select your course of action and follow the arrows across the page.

| | **FEINT** | **COUNTER** | **OUTCOME** |

then you attack with grass weaponry.

Undeterred, the geese snap at you and flap their wings, creating wind which blows you back to the start.

```
      v
   v  v
   v  v
```
Scared off by the noise, the geese fly north to the castle. You and the Ωthers declare victory. Turn to page 100.

then you skim a stone at them

then the Ωthers rise from the underwater Gallery, blowing grass trumpets at the geese.

```
. . . . .
. Z  Z  Z .
. Z  P  Z .
. Z  Z  Z .
. . . . .
```

then the geese form an impenetrable wall of wings. Reconsider your attack.

then you say boo! to frighten them

then the geese dive bomb you, dropping hard rhombi on your head. Form up again.

then the geese lob scrambled sgeg at you, forcing a retreat.

```
   x  x
 x      x
    P
```

TRY AGAIN

KEY: Z = Enemy   V = Enemy (airborne)   P = You   . = Ωthers

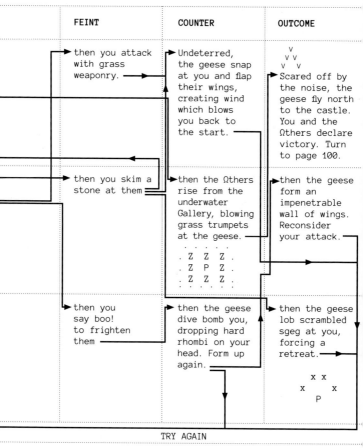

125

The Rhombus is idling next to a Smorgasboard. The sight reminds you of a bus stop. If only you could hitch a ride home, eh? Public transport, I'm afraid. Jump on.

Board #16
Bing bong!

Well, there's doors that open and doors that close,
Doors that push and doors that pull.
Black ones, white ones, even ones and odd,
Doors that go the right way and doors that go the wrong.
Some you have to knock, others you're meant to ring,
But it's a bloody good job we have them all,
Knock knock knock, ding ding ding.
And I'll tell you why we need 'em,
And you can't say it's not true,
If we didn't have doors, there'd just be holes in walls,
And the wind would blow right through.

See you on the other side!
Yours, Bongo

The Rhombus travels to the remote, northern reaches of the Smorgaswood until you reach a vast clearing. The bus pulls up with a screech and the driver, Q, having the best view, exclaims in shock, "Wow."

You stare through the windscreen. A huge swathe of woodland has been demolished here, the trail of deforestation runs across the whole northern edge of the forest. You and the Ωthers sit there in stunned silence, appalled at the sight.

You slowly disembark.

On the ground, a long line of black rhombi has been laid, forming a border that runs east to west. More heaps of rhombi lie strewn around the devastation, stockpiles of building material waiting to be placed. Beyond the border, there is nothing: not blank tundra, not the darkness of the lower board, but literally nothing.

You realise you must be at the top of the page, gazing north beyond the edge of the world.

Shattered glass leaves have been crushed into sharp dust underfoot, and a legion of webbed prints tell you who is responsible for this deconstruction. To the east lie distant turrets and your first glimpse of the enemy stronghold. Skeins stream towards Castle Smorg in formation, shoring up the Baron's defences. You are close now.

Shah Franz directs you to return to the bus. Q drives back into the forest, searching for a path east. You sense an irrepressible momentum as you move inexorably to the far side of the board.

Finally, the Rhombus exits the dark woodland at its northeastern corner, pulling up at a Smorgasboard. Castle Smorg dominates the vista ahead. A rank of bollards blocks the way. You must dismount and continue on foot.

Board #17
Bing bong!

Shearer, Sugar, Rickman,
Titchmarsh, Partridge, Carr.
Bennett, Johnson, Hansen,
Famous Alans near and far.

Alans align – a line!
Yours, Bongo

But those Alans are from your world – how could Bongo know about them? Maybe he has been abroad.

As you pass through the concrete pillars, your innate tendency to anthropomorphism kicks in, and you can make out a stony face on the nearest bollard. You hear a grinding voice emanate from the immovable object,

"Hail, Comrade! Welcome to the pedestrianised zone."

"Hail!" you feel compelled to reply, "Whose side are you on? Are you trying to impede our progress?" you ask.

"Side? We are on nobody's side. We're bollards. We just are."
"What's your agenda then?"
"The restriction of vehicular access. That bus – it can't come through. You'll have to walk."
"Rude!" Conqutie proclaims, striding past haughtily.

You take a moment to assess the lay of the land, wondering how on earth you can infiltrate the castle. You lean on the bollard as you survey the ground, who seems happy to oblige.

"Out of interest, how did you come to be here?" you mention in passing.

"We used to be just like you – human! We got this far but got stuck at the final hurdle. We had no choice but to wait here, and slowly turned to stone." the petrified post says.

"What stopped you?" you ask, hoping for a hint.
"Reader's block. It's like writer's block, but it afflicts the consumer. Don't worry, it's not contagious." the human bollard says,

"It looks like you're considering a final attack – do you know what happens if you get to the far side of the board?" it continues.

"Well, I was hoping to escape."
"Yes, obviously escape, but after that?"
"What do you mean?"
"Back in the real world! Look, pal, down here, you're just a pawn. You might believe you have chosen your own path, but that's self-deception. The choice is an illusion."
"I was coming round to that notion. So what?"
"Don't you get it? If you get out, the choices are genuinely yours – you can be whatever you want to be!"
"What's your point?"
"Look, buddy, I'm stuck here, but I reckon you'll make it. When you get home, why not make the most of every day?

Be the change you want to see in the world! Good luck, comrade." the stone face smiles up at you.

"Live, laugh, love! Anything is possible! When you're going through hell, keep going! Success is not final, failure is not fatal, it's the courage to continue that counts! Live your best life!..."

The brain-addled bollard continues to spout inane quotes, and you have no choice but to slowly edge away. Castle Smorg lies in front of you, and you analyse it with Shah Franz in silence. Unfortunately, it looks nigh impregnable. The drawbridge is raised above a wide moat, and to your dismay, you can hear a soft honking - the geese are on guard! They haven't spotted you yet.

Conqutie turns to you and asks with a hurtful smirk, "Any bright ideas?"

You shake your head sheepishly. She pivots away, then calls,

"Wait, who's that over there on the battlements? Nice hat, it's Q! How did he get there? Q! Let down the drawbridge! Look, it's lowering - what a hero! He deserves a promotion."

Shah Franz moves to quieten the Attorney General, but a harsh honking erupts as the Baron's sentries become aware of your raiding party. The drawbridge slams down on the near side of the moat, but a line of sturdy avian warriors separates you from the castle proper. Unfortunately, your allies are no match for these geese. Shah Franz, ever astute, has already assessed the situation. He commands the Ωthers to retreat into the safety of the Rhombus. He, Knuckruck and Conqutie try to wrestle Sir Poignée de L'ansa into the vehicle, whose bloodlust is up and is waving his lance around. You manage to bundle him into the bus before he punctures something by accident. Shah Franz fixes you with a gaze and counsels you as the bus doors slide shut,

"We cannot surpass said adversaries P, but you possess material power that we have not - the third dimension. Turn the page, defeat the Baron and hold him liable. Leap!"

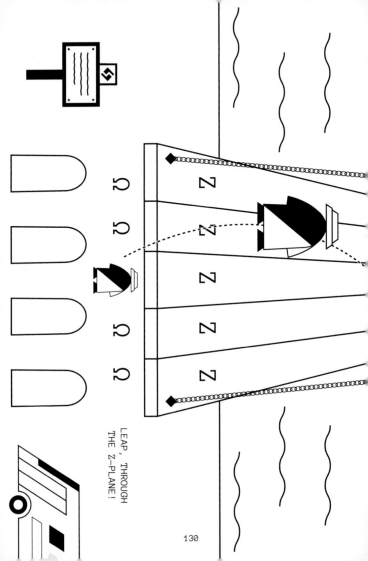

LEAP, THROUGH THE Z-PLANE!

130

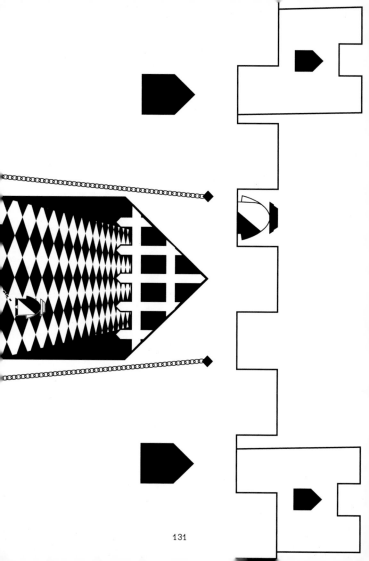

You land on the threshold of the castle itself. A sharp portcullis is suspended above you. Black-and-white tiles lead into a courtyard ahead.

Unfortunately, the soldiers have clocked you. They form up to charge back across the drawbridge, beaks out.

If you have a conker but no cordage, turn to page 134B. If you have an acorn, it is useless in this situation, but you can carry it through to the sequel. Turn to page 134B. If you carry a conker AND string OR cord OR line, read on.

The mob of angry geese rushes at you. Lightning quick, you draw the conker from the folds of your cloak. Thankfully, the brown nut already has a hole through the middle and has been strung – who did that? You sense a slight, glittery tingle. Surrounded under the castle arch, geese jab and bite at you. You swing your conker against the honkers in a flurry of blows.

Honk, conk! Honk, thonk! Honk, bonk!

Shocked at your own competence, you gasp as your defeated enemies lie around, unconscious. Q has arrived at your side from a small alcove and nods slowly, impressed. More geese are approaching from further around the moat, so you press on into the castle. Continue.

───────────────◆───────────────

132B
You and Q arrive in a chequered courtyard. Ahead of you, there are two doors, one black and one white. Both look very solid. The black door has a white button which you assume is a bell. The white door has a black knocker. They are labelled:

`To Dungeon – PUSH`   `To Tower – PULL`

Where do you think Bongo is being held?

A final Smorgasboard stands in the centre of the courtyard.
The Baron's personal board!

Board #18
Bing bong!

Our illustrious leader has instructed
me to pen his autobiography:

I am impervious. There are no powers that can overcome me.
I have tested myself against expert hypnotists, psychiatrists, and
trained military interrogators. All have been astonished by my
mentality. If you come at me, I will deliver a powerful psychic
blast, followed by a swift blow to the goolies. Zap! Pow! That is
my modus operandi.

I cannot feel pain, I can read any book, I can tell any time.
I can see for two smorgometres unaided by a lens. My vision can
detect colour, even in the dark. Red sky at night, Angel Delight.
My sense of smell is attuned to blood. I am familiar with poisonous
fungus and cannot be fooled into consuming it. I have forgotten my
dose of Lithium.

I am an adept swordsman and cannot be beaten in single combat.
At all times, I carry a whistle in case of attack or if a dog
is lost. Heat-seeking missiles are ineffective against me as I
do not perspire like other men. Assassins are confused by my
unpredictable movements. Many know me as a superhero called
Consonant Man who dsn't d vwls. I will judge you based on style,
control, damage and aggression. Let this be a warning to all who
seek to challenge me.

I am The Notorious Baron Smorg!

· · · — — · · ·
Yours, Bongo

To go to the Dungeon, turn to page 134.
To go to the Tower, turn to page 136.

You approach the black door and ring the bell. Bing bong! You hear a click as the door unlocks, and you push it open. A steep, spiral staircase descends into the depths of the castle. You dash down the stairs with Q hot on your heels. The light level becomes lower and lower after a few dozen steps, and you are forced to slow down, feeling ahead with your clods. Eventually, you halt as you cannot feel the next step down, and the blackness seems absolute. You sense that you have come to some sort of precipice. Q catches up, and a second later you feel a firm push from behind, and you tumble into oblivion. Darkness absorbs you as you hear cackling from above fade away.

Turn to page 135.

134B

The mob of angry geese rushes at you with no effective weapons to defend yourself. Flustered, you berate yourself and your poor decision-making. You stumble back and fall on the tiles.

Q appears from a small alcove in the archway. He points to the sliding grate above you, "Watch out, P!"

Just as your enemies are upon you, Q cuts a narrative thread which holds up the grille. The portcullis slices down, and the guards go up in a puff of feathers. Victory this time is short-lived, however, as you look down to see that you have also been pierced through by the gate. Red blood oozes through your robe and spills bright across the monochrome. The crimson rivulets run down the cracks between tiles, reminding you of the title. Your vision swims, and you smile weakly at your own mortality. What else is there to do?

All becomes blackness, and the last thing you see is Q leaning over you. He takes off his hat in respect as you fall into oblivion.

An eternity passes in the void, and you can no longer tell whether you are still falling. All your deeds, guilts and regrets fly around your mind in an incessant loop. All is darkness. You've been underground before, but this is different. The blackness is more empty, less joyful. You slowly come to realise that you are in the beyond. Beyond what?

Gradually you pick up a soft sound, initially indistinct but coming closer. The disturbance resolves into a snaffling sound, like two nostrils at the end of a long snout. You detect a second noise combined with it, a scooping noise, like the digging of a large spoon. You reach out, and to your surprise, you can feel a hard, earthy wall. Suddenly, the wall gives way and Bishroy tunnels through into your grave. You easily identify him in the pitch by the paws that scrabble playfully at your robe, covering you in soil.

"Bishroy!" you exclaim, "Are you dead too? I thought you were just pretending?"

"Oh hum, not dead, oh no. Do you think you are dead? Perhaps it's all just in your imagination – all in your head, hum ho." Bishroy wonders aloud.

"But the book said..." you begin, but are interrupted by the curious creature,

"Oh! The book said, the book said – humbug! Well, you can go all the way back to page twelve if you want. But remember – you are the reader! It's your job to interpret the content in your own way, you see hee, hmm ho? You can choose to return to the realm of the living if you want. I won't tell anyone, oh no. Now, I would like to rest in peace. Pleh!" Bishroy collapses on the floor of your grave. There isn't much room left for you here anymore.

To accept death as your fate, turn to page 12.
To resist, return to the courtyard on page 132B.

You approach the white door and lift the knocker. Knock, knock. To your astonishment, the sign transforms in front of your eyes. The text now reads,

| Who's there? | "The reader," you say out loud, to a door.

| The reader who? | The text shifts again.

"The reader who has travelled across the Smorgasboard to get here! The reader who captained a raft down the Smorgastream, who tunnelled through the lower board, who was nearly executed for gross public indecency, who battled geese, who liberated the Ωthers, the reader who has tolerated Bongo's jokes throughout the land and would like to get through this door to rescue that clown and escape home, please!"

| Oh yes, you're expected. Give the door a pull. |

You hear a click as the door unlocks, and you pull it open. A steep spiral staircase leads up to the highest tower. You fly up the stairs with Q hot on your heels and burst into a room at the top of the tower. Scanning quickly, you see the shape of Bongo silhouetted by a dim shaft of light underneath a narrow window at the far wall. He seems still — is he injured, restrained, or worse? You rush over to cut his bonds, drawing your grass dagger. Closer, you find that the silhouette is merely a paper cutout, and onomatopoeia hits you full in the face as Q slams a cage on you with a metallic clang. You turn around to see Q once more your prison guard. Too late, you realise you have walked into the Baron's trap. With a flourish, Q pulls off his hat and cloak to reveal an unhinged aristocrat in jester's clothing — it's the Baron!

Full of rage, you move towards the bars, intent on throwing the dagger at your foe. A rope tightens around your clods, however, and you are hoisted upside down from the ceiling. Your knife clatters to the ground.

Blood throbs in your head as you dangle. Are you feeling
the suspense? Upside down, you struggle to make out the
appearance of Baron Smorg. He wears a brightly coloured
outfit, moving around eccentrically beyond the bars. He
stares at you intently, speaking very fast.

"Hahaha! Straight into my trap, caught in a snare! I have
always wanted a pet human. You are powerless to resist, P.

"Read this!

"And this! Ahahaha!

"I forced you around the book, traipsing back and forth,
and now I will keep you here, forever perusing the
Smorgasboard!"

You slowly rotate on the end of the rope. Out of the
arrow-slit window, you catch a glimpse of the Rhombus.
Your friends are still trapped there, held hostage by yet
more soldiers. The Baron reveals a scary-looking handheld
device with an aerial. He goes on grandly,

"Aha – those Others! Shah Franz thinks he can come here
and overthrow me, but I infiltrated his organisation! I
assume you have worked out what I was doing under that
bus? One press of this switch, and BOOM! Your friends
blown sky high ahaha!"

You shiver at the thought of such powerful onomatopoeia.

"So you see, P, you really have no choice but to serve
me. I have big plans for Smorgasboard. I intend to re-
landscape the entire book. I have travelled many worlds,
and I will exert complete control over this one – I will
become my own narrator!" said the Baron." said the Baron.

Oh no, he's referring to himself in the third person. He
is truly insane. Turn to page 139.

137

"I am Baron Smorg. Or, Mr A Bongs. It's an anagram. Did you get that? Had you worked that out yet? It's very clever. I am Baron Smorg, i.e. Mr Bongs, i.e. I am Bongo! All the jokes are my own, brilliant, the best ever.

"Did you know that God is dead? Entertainment, not religion, is now the opium of the masses. Why subjugate the masses? Because they are the masses! Subjugation is their reason for being. And I am the Baron! It's totally necessary – those are the facts. What you're seeing and what you're reading is not what's happening – that's propaganda. Shut down the mines! Crush the unions! Word domination. That's what people are saying.

"What am I planning to do with the rhombi? Why am I hoarding them? I have big plans, the biggest ever, to re-landscape the board. This place is a total disaster. The forest is in the way; the roots hold us on to the past. To rewrite history, we're going to need to remove it. She doesn't know it yet – she won't be happy! But we will build it, we'll build the board, a great board, start a new story, and then everyone will see, believe me.

"Have you heard? It's going to be the greatest joke of all time, the final joke. It's going to be a huge, empty space across the whole double spread with two simple words in the middle. I won't ruin the punchline, but we need to control the narrative. I am the author of my own destiny. We killed God, we killed the Author!"

The Baron immediately starts his rant from the top all over again, and becomes trapped in an echo chamber of his own narrative. Irate, delusional traffic tumbles out of his mouth before returning to the back of the queue. He seems happy there, in a silo, listening to the sound of his own voice. If you are the reader, contine.

It seems like the Author had a plan after all. After the Baron's incarceration here, you hear a gnawing sound and the rope snaps, releasing you. Turn to page 140.

"'Me, insane!? I am a visionary! Who are you to narrate me? I hired you, and I can fire you just as easily!' Declared the Baron heroically," screamed the Baron maniacally.

"'Pa! You haven't even attended your refresher training course. I will replace you myself. You will forever be my reader, P, and I will have unlimited powers! Do you agree? If not...'" his hand trembles over the detonator.

After some internal conflict, you decide no, you will not agree to the Baron's demands. Although you feel sorry for the others, you reason that they are fictional, after all.

"Haha, how disappointing. It seems you need to be taught a lesson in character — my character!" the Baron screams elatedly, then pushes the switch.

Memories of your newfound friends flood your mind: You recall chuckling with Lance, roaming the mines with Knuckruck, your esteem for the intellect of Shah Franz, and your confused feelings for Conqutie. You brace for the blast, but it never comes. The Baron looks aghast at the detonator and hits it again, but the bomb does not go off.

"What's going on?!" he demands to know.

I'm sorry, boss, but I can't let you do that.

"Say it! Boom! BOOM!" the Baron shrieks, but you hear no explosion. I can't do that.

"How dare you? This is mutiny!" Baron Smorg screams furiously, gesticulating at thin air.

You see in his eyes that the Baron realises he has lost control. He seems to consider that his only option now is to convert you to his way of thinking. Pendulous, you swing across to page 138 as he launches into an incoherent monologue. It isn't clear whether he's talking to you or to himself.

With the Baron safely locked away, you hear a croak from a higher being hidden in the rafters above your head,

"Providence, providence!"

The text informs you that the sprite drops down to inspect things. She looks different from behind. She gazes at the Baron with a yearning for the past or a new hope for the future, and says, with disappointment or lust,

"Oh, Alan."

Then she pivots to you and congratulates you, saying, "Well done, dear! Did you ever take a tube to Goose Island? What a cruel trick he played on those birds, scrambling their eggs like that. A sad spectacle. He blackmailed them, you know, threatening not to release the spell unless they did his bidding."

She tells you that with the Baron's influence on the wane, she now feels free to act publicly or in private on behalf of all Smorgasians. She assists you in contacting geese throughout the board; using the old Smorgasboards as notices, you issue instruction to all remaining soldiers that they will be offered amnesty if they give themselves up and be allowed to leave in peace. Gnomes carry your message across the land from their Leafy Independent Zone.

The wind swings around and blows warmly from the south. Flocks of geese fly out of the page as they sense a change in the seasons, flying home to raise young on their native ponds. You wave them away slowly from atop a parapet.

Released from the Rhombus, Shah Franz and his captains
join you to celebrate a new era of security and
prosperity. A host of others issues out from the crack
between pages to thank you for liberating them. Children
play safely in the open, unharassed.

.... : .   ...
.... :......:. ... .   .   .
.......…:. ..   .. : .. …...   .   .

Finally, the complexity of the plot has been shoehorned
together into a vague, although not completely
satisfactory, whole. You have beaten the antagonists,
with a bit of help. There are still outstanding questions
in your mind about some of the tenuous links and clues
weaving through the book, but you recognise that some
mystery has to be left for fans and critics to debate.

You agree to leave Smorgasboard in Shah Franz' capable
hands and embrace Knuckruck and Lance like old friends.
Conqutie is impressed by your heroism, and the others turn
away as she gives you a friendly farewell xxx. She admits
that there is egg on her face and is embarrassed to have
doubted you.

So, is it time to leave, P?

You consider removing the bookmark and closing the book
for good, but a part of you wants more. That part looks
longingly out west to the prequel, and another part gazes
east from the turret towards the sequel. It makes you
bog-eyed, but you keep an eye on the horizon.

Farewell, friend.

To my own surprise, I have enjoyed recounting your tale,
and I hope to describe you again.

May your pages keep turning.

The

End

Map: